Fai**lure**
Whistlebl**owing in healthcare**

Failure to Care:
Whistleblowing in Healthcare

Kyle J. Gilrain

RAMBLER
PUBLISHING

Printed in the United States of America

Library of Congress Cataloging-in-Publication Data:
Kyle J. Gilrain
Failure to Care: Whistleblowing in Healthcare/Gilrain, Kyle
Includes bibliographic references and index.

ISBN
978-1-7372705-0-8 (Paperback Edition)
978-1-7372705-3-9 (Hardback Edition)
978-1-7372705-1-5 (Ebook Edition)
978-1-7372705-2-2 (Ebook Edition)
978-1-7372705-4-6 (Audiobook Edition)

Library of Congress Control Number: 2021939315

RAMBLER
PUBLISHING

RamblerPublishing.com

SAN: 992-2628

Dedication

This book is dedicated to my late father, James M. Gilrain. He was a loving father, best friend, mentor, source of great inspiration, and impeccable role model. He was a tireless advocate for those less fortunate. He always spoke up for the marginalized and disadvantaged. Countless lives were improved by his work. It is a loss that can never be replaced, but he continues to walk beside me as an ethicist and advocate. He taught me how to dream.

Acknowledgements

I wanted to take a moment to thank some of the people who helped and encouraged me through the many transitions I have faced on my whistleblower path.

Foremost, I would like to thank my mother, Rita Gilrain. Her unwavering support and encouragement to always do the right thing has been an amazing inspiration to me and helped me through many life transitions. She has never questioned why I spoke up and has always encouraged me to do so. She is a strong woman and a great role model. She is the rock behind my moral fortitude.

Heartfelt thank you to Mary West, her husband Chris, and their three children Quincy, Maya, and Avery. Always by my side since the age of two, I have been able to count on Mary to be there in both good times and bad – far too many of each to mention here. Special thank you to Quincy West, whose blunt and candid words prompted me to get moving to start writing this book – and to follow it through to completion.

Similarly, Carol-ann Ricardo for the persistent encouragement to write this book and the gentle prodding for progress updates. I cherish our decades-long friendship and the fact that she is a tireless advocate for accountability in improving the lives of children and communities.

Catherine Jordan for always being there to talk me through many painful transitions. Truly the communications expert who has always helped me communicate my message and encouraged my path forward – wherever it led.

Dr. Christine Nevada Michael for taking a chance on me and believing in me from the day I stepped foot on the campus of Southern Vermont College. Thank you for encouraging my authenticity in the pages of this book and for being an exceptional mentor and friend throughout the years.

My sincere gratitude to Brian Hemmert, who has always shown me that executive leaders in healthcare can govern with both ethics and business acumens. Always the exceptional healthcare leader with a steadfast belief in strength-based and trauma-informed care. Thank you for the ongoing belief in my work, the long-term friendship, and doing the right thing by patients – always.

Linda Siemer – a tireless advocate for the betterment of children and vulnerable adults. Countless individuals and families are better off for the work that she does. I cannot thank her enough for being such a large part of my whistleblower journey and for being a partner in stopping some of the most egregious examples of abuse in healthcare institutions I have personally witnessed.

For the victims of abuse in our troubled-teen and healthcare systems, thank you for sharing your stories and helping to bring awareness to institutional abuse. Your stories truly punctuate the need for healthcare whistleblowers.

Thank you to the many moral and ethical healthcare workers, who I have had the pleasure of working with throughout my career.

Finally, thank you to Leslie Barber for her editorial assistance that has touched and improved every page of this book. I cannot thank you enough.

Contents

Contents

Preface

In many respects, the trajectory of my personal path and career path were predisposed and aligned to become that of an advocate, ethicist, and practitioner concerned with the well-being of both vulnerable and marginalized individuals. As far as I knew growing up, no member of my family worked in the healthcare profession. Indeed, both of my parents were educators who shared a belief that through education, of any kind, came opportunity. My parents also both shared a moral belief that we have a responsibility, as a society, to lift up underserved and marginalized individuals. My parents truly never hesitated to speak up against wrongdoing of any kind. Indeed, both of my parents had a strong moral compass and fostered this basic tenet in all three of their children.

My father's moral compass drove him to aspire to become influential in the ending of racism. Upon his death, I learned that he had written "to be instrumental in the ending of racism" as one of his three life goals. My father was raised in a school system torn apart by race riots. He later became an administrator in that very same school system which saw its fair share of racial strife throughout the 1970s and 1980s. The racial tensions in the town, however, dated back to the 1920s, when white people in town stabbed and murdered people of color and burned black churches to the ground. Racial tensions were, indeed, seared into the fabric of this town from very early on and permeated until my father tried to extinguish them during his long tenure working in the school system there.

When my father became a school administrator in the 1960s, he created the school's first human relations coordinator position. This new position served to create and provide multicultural events and foster diversity and inclusion in both the school and community. Although many didn't know it at the time, in creating this position he was a forerunner in this arena. My father was also a coach who used athletics as a great community unifier as well. Additionally, he used his coaching platform to bring the community together and to foster a common pride in the diversity of the town. He was a phenomenal and passionate public speaker. He used all of these skills to unify his community.

My mother was very supportive of my father's efforts to help marginalized students, people of color, and their families. She was most passionate about the students whom most other educators had grown frustrated with and given up on. My mother was never one to cast people aside, regardless of how damaged or broken others thought they were. She was one of the rare educators who enjoyed the kids who were destined to spend a good portion of their summer in summer school. In fact, she taught summer school for several years. She never once gave up on them, just as she has never given up on me.

My educational path started quite tenuous. In high school I was often characterized as someone who did not work up to his potential. When most of my friends were applying to colleges, I found myself with fewer options. My mother found a small private liberal arts college in Vermont that seemed to cater to those who did not realize their potential in high school. My older brother had also attended the school and really liked it, so I applied and was accepted as well.

While at Southern Vermont College, my academic advisor was a woman named Gloria Alexander. A petite older woman who fostered great fortitude in her students, she frequently pushed students to reach their potential, creating lifelong learners and advocates. She often, and patiently, nudged me beyond my comfort zone and fostered a never-give-up attitude with respect to using the social work profession as a catalyst to help others. After graduating from Southern Vermont College, I went on to earn my master's degree from the Columbia University School of Social Work.

Similarly, in my professional path, I have served in progressively more responsible positions in all facets of the mental healthcare industry. I have served as a psychotherapist, healthcare leader, clinical supervisor, ethicist, and patient advocate in multiple healthcare settings. I have provided education and trainings on salient topics within the healthcare field and have worked the full continuum of healthcare settings to include:

Residential Treatment Centers (both secure and
non-secure)

Incarceration Facilities (juvenile and adult
  prison settings)
Inpatient Psychiatric Units (child and adult)
Outpatient Psychiatric Units (child and adult)
Partial Hospitalization Programs (child and adult)
Medical Hospitals (all ages)
Private Practice (all ages)

While attending Southern Vermont College, I served as a mental health tech/residential counselor in a residential treatment program for adolescents. This early front-line experience informs my respect, and the expectations I have, of front-line staff to this day. Upon completion of my master's degree, I have served in several leadership positions in both inpatient and outpatient settings respectively.

My healthcare leadership experience includes management positions within large and complex health systems that each have operated hundreds of facilities across the U.S. I have served in multiple senior leadership positions including the Director of Clinical Services, Director of Performance Improvement, Director of Outpatient Services, and Director of Residential Services. In these positions I was responsible for contributing to, and adhering to, policies and best-practice models of care that spanned across the entire continuum of care in multiple complex delivery systems.

I have also had the opportunity to write grants and direct outcomes studies in multiple settings. I have written grants to fund research, outcome studies, and to provide specialized mental health treatment. I have directed outcomes studies that include a comparative analysis of the cultural sensitivity of two different (intrusive/thorough and less intrusive/introductory and cursory) mental health intake procedures, as well as, outcomes studies of sexual offender treatment programs and domestic violence treatment programs respectively.

In addition to my formal education, I have both received and provided formal professional training as well. I have been trained in Prolonged Exposure Therapy by the Center for Deployment Psychology and in Structural Family Therapy by the Minuchin Center for the Family. The trainings I have provided include such salient topics as ethics in healthcare, cascading transgressions, differential diagnosis in mental health, and the identification of signs and symptoms of sexual abuse in children.

In each professional position I have held, I have fought to serve as a patient advocate and have honored the traditions and ethics of my profession. What I have learned from my healthcare experiences is that if we are ever going to improve the healthcare systems in this country the solution will have to be multifarious. Indeed, any significant improvement in healthcare will have to rely on healthcare workers with strong moral fortitude, tenacity, a solid advocacy skill set, and a willingness to toil if we are to effectively change systems from within. Simultaneously, it is also going to take tireless advocates to change laws and work with external systems to improve the framework of accountability for those who fail to care.

Introduction

Failure to Care: Whistleblowing in Healthcare is a culmination of my own research and my experiences advocating and blowing the whistle in multiple work settings. It is also about the subsequent reinventions of my own career. In blowing the whistle, I have lost a lot, gained some, and reinvented myself more than once. I live to write about it – and I also live to regret none of it.

The personal information and experiences I write about in this text are not isolated to any one workplace in particular. In fact, the experiences punctuated in this book span multiple work settings and take place in different types of healthcare facilities. These experiences are not intended as an attack on any individual or any specific agency. In fact, none of the agencies I have worked for are mentioned by facility or company name nor are any individuals mentioned by name. I have changed formal agency names to Agency One, Agency Two, Agency Three, and so on. Names were not omitted to protect any entity or individual. Rather, they were left out to avoid distracting the reader and because I do not wish to use this book for personal grievance. This book is about the patients, clients, and all the people healthcare workers take an oath to protect and treat. This book is a candid discussion about how we, as healthcare workers, often fall short in accomplishing this purpose and how we can improve upon healthcare delivery.

The primary intent of this book is to educate and encourage advocates and whistleblowers. It is a call for people to come together and be united in defense of our respective codes of ethics. It is a call to challenge wrongdoing and to simultaneously provide a framework for doing so. Most important, however, it is a call to unite in reducing abuse in our healthcare institutions. It is a call to not sacrifice our own morals and ethics in deference to some figurehead asserting his or her own megalomania over others.

Additionally, some of the tactics and techniques I have personally witnessed or utilized have not been broadly shared until this text. I believe readers will find these tactics and techniques useful, and it is my hope that people will put them to good use in their quest to protect clients and patients from malfeasance.

The detailed how-tos found in this book are often missing from other whistleblower articles and books. In my conversations with countless colleagues, I have learned that many healthcare professionals are not aware of how to effectively blow the whistle and create their strongest possible case. As one colleague once aptly said to me, very few people know how to put together a "packet." Throughout this book, the "packet" refers to the body of evidence that advocates have collected throughout their employment that will help them present the best possible cases to support their cause. Simply put, the packet is the body of evidence that supports your claims.

This packet also helps establish a timeline of events that

can serve to become very important as the particular cause that you are pursuing progresses. The documentation you collect for the packet becomes particularly important because one piece of documentation may appear innocuous, but when used collectively to complete a packet of material you can often establish a well-documented pattern of malfeasance. The packet is the body of evidence to support your whistleblower and advocacy efforts.

Although, a great body of literature about whistleblowers does exist, I felt compelled to write this book because much of what has been written not only excludes the "how-to," but also largely concentrates on the negative consequences of whistleblowing in general. There are several salient reasons I want to correct this narrative and to help people become more effective advocates for patients in their healthcare careers. The reasons to become a more effective advocate for yourself and for patients are multifarious. These reasons will be detailed throughout this book as I discuss the impact the failure to act has on others and how to minimize the impact speaking up might have on you.

Indeed, whistleblowing is a lonely and isolating business, but it is my belief that it should not be this way. In my own experience, part of the reason whistleblowing is so isolating is because so many people have created their own self-talk to justify turning a blind eye to the problematic behavior of colleagues and agencies. This book is intended to challenge this self-talk.

One of the most common reasons people talk themselves into remaining silent about wrongdoing includes the very real fear of retaliation from supervisors. In fact, much of what has been written about whistleblowers to date heavily emphasizes the consequences to the whistleblower. The same literature often fails to discuss the far-reaching consequences to human lives when we don't blow the whistle. This is particularly true in healthcare settings where we treat chronically ill and sometimes vulnerable (mentally and medically) people. Indeed, many are aware of the retaliation whistleblowers receive when blowing the whistle and, in the whistleblower literature, little is said about the long-term impact the acquiescence of wrongdoing has on our patients. Patient fraud and abuse have a pronounced and profound impact on the lives of those we are responsible for protecting.

Moreover, the healthcare whistleblower's reality is more complex and intrinsically different than that of other industries. In healthcare, elevating business interests over patient care often serves to lower the access to care and, similarly, the quality of care (Waldman 2003). Simply put, business decisions in healthcare cannot be made the same way they are in other industries. Lowering costs in nursing, for example, will directly impact the timeliness and quality of care to patients. This delay of care to patients leads to substandard care, malfeasance, medical errors and even patient death. Waldman (2003) broaches the need for different leadership models for the lamentable healthcare industry.

Organizational power can be strong and difficult to penetrate. In my experience, so few people know how to effectively challenge powerful organizations, and this lack of challenge serves to advance corporate marauders who infect institutions and cause harm to patients and clients. Additionally, when push comes to shove, so few people are willing to risk jobs and careers for the health and well-being of patients, many of whom are often complete strangers to the healthcare worker. Many healthcare practitioners have succumbed to, and have been subjugated by, profane figureheads with mock morals. It is my hope that this book provides some ideas on protecting yourself from these abusive figureheads.

That said, sometimes protecting yourself does not always mean remaining in your position or even in your agency. Throughout my career, protecting myself has meant different things. When you blow the whistle and advocate, I have found that there are often three ways it could go.

1. Advocating and being heard – Advocating and being heard is the ideal scenario. This means protecting your patients, or clients, and then everything proceeds on nicely.
2. Making it better for the next person – Making it better for the next person means putting forth the best advocacy to make the place, and your position, better for the next person who takes it. In some cases, you move on after speaking out and the agency resents you for it but then still makes the called for improvements.
3. Ongoing advocacy and whistleblowing. Tireless advocacy and whistleblowing mean relentless advocacy until the place either changes leadership

and/or closes. If the problem in the agency is isolated to leadership, you can rest after the leadership changes. In other cases, the problems have infected the entire institution, necessitating its closure.

Throughout my career, I have been fortunate to have experienced all three of the aforementioned outcomes. Lastly, there is often a sense of gloom and doom in the literature about whistleblowers and we, just as we frequently tell patients, need to adapt, grow, and sometimes reinvent ourselves. If you are prepared for this, it will help reduce the risk of your becoming what we read about throughout much of the whistleblower literature.

While there is truth to the doom-and-gloom narrative, it does not have to be that way if we effectively encourage more advocates and whistleblowers. There is, indeed, strength in numbers—the very premise of labor unions. Labor unions utilize collective bargaining to advocate for employees as a whole and limit the exposure of individuals to be targeted for adverse actions because the individual doesn't have to be an advocate who acts unilaterally. Whistleblowers often feel like they are alone in doing the right thing. When people collectively stand up for the same set of values, it becomes increasingly difficult for unethical employers to target individuals for retaliation.

That said, the whistleblower landscape can be complex and confusing. There are moral, ethical, and legal reasons to blow the whistle. The whistleblower process can also become quite overwhelming. There is so much whistleblowers can learn to increase their effectiveness, but that is often left out of the curriculum of most healthcare educational programs and, too often, the scholarly literature. This book endeavors to educate and prepare whistleblowers for tireless advocacy in meeting the needs of those we serve.

Chapter One

The Whistleblower Landscape

For many, whistleblowing falls within the scope of morality and is grounded in individuals with a strong set of moral beliefs. This can be described as the moral model. Moral whistleblowing can be characterized as a unique type of whistleblowing by individuals who consider themselves "moral agents" and are motivated by a firm belief in their moral obligation to do the right thing (Watts and Buckly 2015). Similarly, Bouville (2008, p. 579) adds, "Morality rejects the idea of choice and the interests of the professional as immoral." Brown (2008) describes the whistleblower as acting beyond his own interest and defines the whistleblowing as "disclosures by organization members about matters of 'public interest' – that is, suspected or alleged wrongdoing that affects more than the personal or private interests of the person making the disclosure" (Brown, 2008, p. 8).

Callahan and Collins (1992, p. 939) further describe a whistleblower as "a person who discloses the illegal or unethical activity of an employer or colleague." This disclosure can be both internal or external. Indeed, whistleblowing is commonly defined as "the disclosure by organization members (former or current) of illegal, immoral or illegitimate practices under the control of their employers, to persons or organizations that may be able to effect action" (Near & Miceli, 1985, p. 4).

For healthcare professionals, there is often little, if any, difference between whistleblower and advocate. Indeed, for many healthcare professionals, advocacy and whistleblowing are unstinting parts of what we do. Greene and Latting (2004) explain whistleblowing as "a special form of advocacy," and many healthcare professionals, at least marginally, recognize the impact that a failure to act has on the lives of the people we serve. That said, whistleblowing often contradicts our fundamental beliefs about organizations and leadership.

Jackall (1988, p. 109-110), in his book *Moral Mazes: The World of Corporate Managers*, punctuates the moral maze that is inherent in some work ethics. This maze incorporates a firm belief in some basic key principles:

1. You never go around your boss.
2. You tell your boss what he wants to hear, always.
3. You drop subjects your boss wants dropped.
4. You are sensitive to your boss's wishes.
5. Your job is not to report something that your boss does not want reported.

The failure to act, advocate, or blow the whistle can leave an indelible mark on the very people healthcare professionals are sworn to protect. For healthcare professionals, failure to protect people in our care is one of the most egregious violations of our own codes of ethics, the professional regulations governing our particular field, and the laws (state and federal) that have been enacted to ensure we do no harm to the people in our care. Worse, failing to act becomes a permanent stain on our own individual and overarching moral compass.

Additionally, whistleblowers are often divided into two distinctly different work sectors. There are public-sector whistleblowers and private-sector whistleblowers. Each work sector affords, or does not afford, different protections for employees. Potential whistleblowers should familiarize themselves with the protections for the sector in which they work.

Public-sector whistleblowers generally work for government entities. Public-sector whistleblowers are often afforded government protections, and there exists a body of federal laws that serve to protect them from workplace retaliation. This does not mean, however, that public-sector whistleblowers can blow the whistle without reprisal. There are many examples of public-sector whistleblowers facing the same consequences and same fate as private-sector whistleblowers.

Private-sector whistleblowers work for private agencies. Some private agencies may receive government funding, but state laws do not always protect whistleblowers from retaliation in private- sector settings. State laws often complicate the rights of whistleblowers in the private sector. For example, states that allow "employee at will" laws may seriously impede the rights of whistleblowers in the private sector. Private-sector whistleblowers struggle to find protection within state laws that sometimes do not exist to protect them. Similarly, "employee at will" does not always mean there is no protection from employers who try to force employees to perform illegal acts. These laws, and the protections they afford or do not afford, vary considerably by state.

The retaliation whistleblowers receive becomes particularly pronounced in the private sector, where laws protecting the whistleblower become increasingly difficult to navigate. As noted above, many of the laws vary by state and can also vary based on where agency funding comes from. In both the public and private sector, it is often best to consult with an employment lawyer to ensure you understand your rights and obligations and to increase your ability to protect yourself. Simply, the whistleblower should have a good understanding of agency policy, protection laws, and a plan that is as thought out as possible.

Greene and Latting (2004), in the journal *Social Work*, offer a framework for whistleblowers. They suggest the following steps:

> "(1) begin with the offending colleague…(2) establish a track record of credibility…(6) assume others in the organization are concerned…(7) obtain corroborating evidence and supporters… (8) keep careful records…(9) use the chain of command…(10) obtain the advice of dispassionate, expert outsiders…(11) obtain emotional support… (12) consider going outside the organization only as a last resort."

It is my personal experience that each of these steps is built upon sage advice.

Whistleblowing can also be a long and arduous process in which the whistleblower often becomes the chief and lone ethicist. Soeken and Soeken (1986) describe the whistleblower process in seven stages defined as: "discovery of the abuse; reflection on what action to take; confrontation with superiors; retaliation; the long haul of legal or other action involved; termination of the case, and going on to a new life." Progressing through the seven phases can sometimes take years.

Within some of the research, there seems to be a general consensus among whistleblowers about the proper order of advocacy. According to Callahan and Collins (1992), in the *Journal of Business Ethics*, the consensus among whistleblowers seems to be: "internal first, law enforcement agencies second, and news media last" (Callahan and Collins 1992, p. 939). Throughout this book I will punctuate how this order is a great guide for helping to build your best body of evidence for your whistleblower packet. Again, building the best packet of information also serves to help you become the best possible advocate both internally and externally.

Agency One

Agency One serves as an example of when the Chief Executive Officer (CEO) is the primary problem in the facility and serves as a great example of how the collection of evidence for your packet is paramount to your effectiveness as a whistleblower.

Agency One was a small private-sector psychiatric hospital that regularly held just over 50 patients. When I was hired here for a leadership position, I was told by the CEO that the person I was replacing was not a team player. He reported that she did not follow directives and that the department was unorganized under her leadership. Paperwork in the department, he said, was statutorily and regularly out of compliance.

Like many hospitals, Agency One began each morning with a flash meeting. In this meeting each respective department broached salient happenings in their department. For my role, I addressed discharge plans and dates for each patient. Noticeably absent from these morning flash meetings was the medical director. Immediately after my hire, I began receiving intense pressure to hold patients until their insurance days were exhausted. For example, if the patient's insurance had approved the patient to be covered for five days, the facility wanted to keep them for exactly five days. Although this pressure tacitly exists in many healthcare facilities, it was stunning to me how overt this pressure was in Agency One. Phrases like "days on the table," to illustrate our leaving money on the table by sending a patient out before his insurance days were exhausted, were commonplace each morning. In fact, the "days on the table" were both reported as, and stated as, "days on the table" each morning by the Director of Utilization Review (UR). If I announced a discharge that would leave a day or two on the table, this set off a chain of comments and events all focused on keeping the patient until the days were exhausted.

The intense pressure to keep patients longer came from the

Chief Financial Officer (CFO), the Chief Executive Officer (CEO), and the Director of Utilization Review (UR). Again, shockingly, this pressure was surprisingly overt and, ironically, the delaying of discharges was not actually in my control. Anyone who works in a hospital setting knows that the social worker does not ever unilaterally determine when a patient is discharged. While our opinion may be valued by the physician, it is the physician who determines the actual discharge date.

When I would announce to the team that a patient was being discharged and what the after-care plan was, the Utilization Review manager would begin with letting us know if we exhausted all the patient's insurance days. If there were any billable days left, the CFO would ask "are you sure there isn't anything else we can do for the patient? Please talk to the doctor and see if we can push this discharge off a day or two (whatever was left on their insurance)." Then the CEO would become more strident in demanding I speak to the doctor about extending the patient stay and report back to him before the patient left. This was all done to assert pressure on me, hoping I would then assert pressure on the doctor, and miraculously disregard the patient's readiness to leave in favor of billing another day or two to exhaust their insurance approval. Any attempt I would make to illustrate that the patient was ready to be discharged, and a solid discharge plan was in place for aftercare, was often met with irreverence.

Similarly, when a patient had exhausted his insurance days, there was a push to get him out the door as soon as possible. In all cases I simply did what I thought was best for the patient clinically. If I truly believed the patient was not ready to go, I would let the doctor know my opinion and why. In almost all cases, however, I was in agreement with the doctor. In most cases my follow-up was simply to let the doctor know about the pressure I faced in morning meetings. There is something particularly unnerving about non-clinical staff – for instance a CFO, making decisions about the best course of treatment for a patient.

At Agency One, leadership's failure to understand the roles did not stop with days on the table. Role ambiguity and people asserting positions outside their scope of practice was a thematic problem there. By way of illustration, Agency One also suffered from bad online reviews. In response, the CEO asked me to get our social work staff to solicit patients for better reviews and testimonials. This idea came to fruition in a business development meeting.

Days after the meeting, the CEO followed up with me by email to see if I had asked my clinical team to come up with any patients who would write us a good review online. He sent this request to me in an email and copied several members of the leadership team. I replied just to him directly and stated that solicitation of patients for testimonials is against the Social Work Code of Ethics. Indeed, section 4.07 of the Social Work Code of Ethics clearly states, "Social workers should not engage in solicitation of testimonial endorsements (including solicitation of consent to use a client's prior statement as a testimonial endorsement) from current clients or from other people who, because of their particular circumstances, are vulnerable to undue influence" (NASW Code of Ethics). The CEO continued to press this issue because he thought my response to him was disdainful. Fortunately, I had also written to the state licensing board for written guidance. For many licensed healthcare professionals, our respective licensing board can be helpful in providing guidance in these areas, and we should not hesitate to reach out to them for guidance and support. This is particularly true since this particular CEO was not a social worker, nurse, or doctor.

In response to his continued pressure for me to get testimonials from patients, I was summoned to a meeting with him and Human Resources. This ethical issue quickly turned into a power struggle with someone who had no idea of the clinical implications of what he was asking. In this meeting I reiterated my statement from the aforementioned email citing the Social Work Code of Ethics. Additionally, I provided my written guidance from the state licensing board, which served to back up my position. This guidance also paralleled the code of ethics to a specific state law I would be violating if I acquiesced to his demands. More specifically, the state licensing board explained that this action falls within the scope of exploitation of patients. Exploitation of patients is a violation of both state and federal law. Most healthcare professionals already understand that we don't ask favors of patients, even if they appear myopic on the surface.

Additionally, in Agency One, I began to notice a pattern of the CEO attacking program directors who spoke up or refused to participate in unethical or illegal actions. Foremost,

I observed that the director I replaced was quite competent and left the department very well organized and well run. I later learned that, much like me, she had ethically clashed with the CEO and had resigned as a result of similar pressures. When I left the facility, the CEO had been there for only 17 months. In that short tenure, he terminated, or caused the departure of, 18 directors spanning six different departments, to say nothing of all the other staff within those departments who left through the revolving door of Agency One. For the whistleblower, so many terminations in a short period of time serve as a warning that you may not have a lot of time to put together a good packet of information and that it is important to be prepared to be terminated shortly after you speak up.

Additionally, some agencies are truly adept at scapegoating staff, creating unrealistic expectations, and assigning blame to those they scapegoat (Schindler 2019), and Agency One was no exception. In fact, some of the meetings at Agency One were so unprofessional and unproductive that the good members of the leadership team dubbed them "assignment of blame meetings." The CEO and CFO of Agency One were so unskilled and unprofessional in leadership that they regularly conducted these meetings with the leadership team as if they were somehow productive and meaningful.

In one such assignment of blame meeting, these profane figureheads would allow our utilization review manager the opportunity to preside and hold court. The meeting would begin with the presentation of a hospital bill that was unpaid for a portion of the patient stay. Usually without any warning she would begin the assign-blame meeting with something like, "Three weeks ago we had one day uncovered with patient x." Most of us, because we were not warned, would have no idea why patient x stayed at the facility for a day unpaid. After all, she was bringing up a past event from three weeks ago that an individual probably never even knew about. This tactic is effective because employees are unprepared to defend themselves. She would then continue with the assignment of blame by asserting causes such as "this is because social services didn't have a discharge plan" or "this is because admissions didn't get the pre-cert on time" or "this is because nursing didn't prepare...." and the blame casting would continue.

The assignment of blame meeting was usually brutal, final, and frequently incorrect. The issue was brought up, blame was declared, and once the blame was assigned, there was no turning back. There were no appeals processes once the blame was assigned to you. The meetings were never about actually identifying a root cause to a problem and then fixing it. If that were the case, we would have been given the problem and time to research and prepare to discuss it. If the meeting were not just simply about assigning blame, we would have been more solution focused. Indeed, these meetings were not about process improvement. In fact, days later, we would often find that the assignment of blame was totally incorrect. For example, after further review, there existed countless examples when UR would lose an insurance appeal at 4:00pm and learn that day was going to be the last day covered by the patient's insurance. Lacking a moral compass, the UR Director would then push to discharge the patient with no viable discharge plan at 5 or 6pm.

For example, this last-minute rush to push patients out the door after 5pm, because their insurance was done paying for their stay, happened several times with homeless patients. As anyone who works with the homeless population knows, you cannot send them to a shelter between 5 and 6:00pm and expect the patient will have a bed to sleep in that night. Sending patients to live in the streets because they had no more insurance days left and hoping for the best is an egregious violation of all ethical principles of practice.

These assignment of blame meetings became so utterly ridiculous that three of us on the leadership team got together and began a concerted effort to turn the meetings positive. Simply, when it was one of our turn to speak, we would bestow compliments on another department for something they did well. Most people took the opportunity to defend their departments and project blame onto another. The three of us always began with something like "I just want to thank...." or "The department did an excellent job with...." and we always picked something positive to say. The look of puzzlement on the face of the CEO and CFO made this well worth it. Most people, however, found the place just too unbearable and poorly run, and this was reflected in the high turnover among all staff.

Some were terminated and others found the retaliation so unbearable that they quit of their own accord. Eventually, the medical director was replaced, and this rapidly increased the cascading transgressions. The new medical director appeared to be willing to do whatever it took to please the CEO.

The new medical director realized that the business office and the utilization review department had begun tracking those days on the table by doctor. This was done so that they could target, for retaliation, the doctors they deemed the biggest offenders in leaving money on the table by not exhausting the patient's covered insurance days. Again, and quite shockingly, this was all done out in the open.

I recall one medical executive board meeting where the doctors were told the days on the table were being tracked by doctor. One of the more ethical psychiatrists turned and glared at me, eyes and mouth wide opened, in total disbelief of how candid the leadership was of this illegal and unethical practice. She simply could not believe that this would be done, let alone said out loud in a meeting. She tendered her resignation shortly thereafter.

In treatment team meeting with the new medical director, he would seek to acquiesce to our utilization review director and CEO. In most facilities, these treatment team meetings include discussions about the patient's problems, course of treatment, and discharge plan. For this medical director, it was simply an opportunity to discuss discharge dates. Worse, when he would tell us the discharge date of the patient, he did so by looking at a spreadsheet that told us each patient's last covered insurance day. For this doctor, the last covered insurance day was always the discharge date. Additionally, this would be true even if the patient just had been admitted that day. This meant that without even getting to know the patients or their treatment issues, he knew they were going to be discharged on the last day of their insurance coverage.

—————

This leads to something I like to call "cascading transgressions." I have provided regular training on cascading transgressions in healthcare organizations where I have served as a leader. Once I was no longer an employee of the organization, however, that training I created was always removed from the training schedule.

The concept of cascading transgressions is as simple as it sounds. Cascading transgressions is an action that a reasonable person might conclude is likely to lead to worse behaviors. Inappropriate relationships and boundary issues with patients often begin with a less serious transgression that cascades into a bigger issue. For example, a therapist providing a patient with his or her personal phone number. Most workplaces would call this inappropriate but not illegal or even, by itself, harmful to the patient. The rationalization includes things like "I was just trying to be helpful" or "I told them to call me before they get depressed again." It is, however, a cascading transgression because it often leads to worse behavior by the employee.

If you closely evaluated any healthcare worker's serious transgressions, you would almost always find that it began with a simple cascading transgression or violation of boundaries. Boundary issues are inherent in healthcare. Due to the nature of the caring relationships we develop with patients, treatment boundaries can be an occupational hazard of all healthcare professionals (Peternelj-Taylor & Yonge 2003). For this reason, regardless of retaliation we might face, it is always important to confront boundary issues in the workplace.

Additionally, retaliation often begins with, and is rooted within, the legal concept of constructive discharge (also referred to as constructive dismissal). Simply, this is when an employer intentionally makes a work situation so intolerable that an employee feels the only viable option is to quit. This can become a very difficult legal tenet to prove. For example, Goldberg (1993, p. 87) explains, in the *ABA Journal*, that a constructive discharge claim "requires proof of both intolerable working conditions and a deliberate effort by the employer to force the employee to resign." He further explains, "This can be demonstrated either by actual evidence of intent by the employer to force the employee out of the job or by circumstantial evidence of intent, including actions that treat the plaintiff differently from his or her coworkers" (Goldberg 1993, p. 87). Proving the element of deliberateness can become very challenging, and this strategy is often unsuccessful in court.

That said, some of the constructive dismissal tactics I have experienced included: unfavorable schedule changes, shifting work expectations, unfavorable work assignments, frequent summoning to meetings about frivolous things, forcing me to do things that could jeopardize my professional license (remember, the act falls on the practitioner and does not always fall on the employer), and similar acts. As you might surmise, many good employers have to do the aforementioned things in the regular course of business, and it does not always fall within the scope of constructive dismissal; this is why the element of deliberateness (actions taken to make an employee quit) becomes difficult to prove.

Temporal proximity is another legal concept that can often help lawyers bolster an argument and perhaps answer the question of whether you were constructively discharged or not. Temporal proximity can help your lawyer identify if your employer retaliated against you for reporting an unlawful activity. When you are blowing the whistle, the packet of evidence with your timeline of events becomes particularly important because it establishes things like temporal proximity.

Temporal proximity is a legal term that describes how close in time specific events occur, and it helps to show if one event was caused by another (Robinson et. al. 2014). Long (2018) articulates that temporal proximity can help determine if the retaliation was "but-for," meaning if your activity (usually a protected action like whistleblowing) caused your employer to take adverse action against you. The longer the time between the action (your advocacy) and reaction (your employer's retaliation), the more likely it is that the courts will determine that the adverse action was caused by something else (Robinson et. al 2014, Long 2018). By way of illustration, if you submit a complaint about an illegal activity of your employer to a supervisor and then experience some adverse action within a day or two, this might be characterized as close temporal proximity.

Beniot and Nagle (2003), in their article on retaliation

claims in the *Employee Relations Law Journal*, caution that one act following another does not always equate to a causal link. As such, they explain other ways to show causation (you complained and they came after you) including: "(1) evidence of differential treatment in the workplace; (2) statistical evidence showing disparate treatment; and (3) comments by the decision maker which intimate a retaliatory mindset" (Beniot and Nagle 2013 p. 39).

In one instance my work schedule was changed by HR the day after I submitted a letter to corporate compliance detailing extensively the illegal and unethical things that had been done at the bequest of the CEO of the facility. In another instance, I was given an unfavorable work assignment minutes after I brought up an issue that contradicted a supervisor in a meeting. But occasionally, I was asked to pick up additional assignments and given unfavorable work as a regular course of agency business, and these actions were not retaliatory at all. It is important to be able to discern the difference, and temporal proximity, and other documented forms of retaliation, can serve as a good barometer to help accomplish this.

Also, it is very important to pay close attention to temporal proximity. Good managers will be able to shroud disciplinary action in close temporal proximity to your expression of concern or your refusal to participate in an illegal act. Other managers, however, will take immediate retaliatory action and hope that you don't know what temporal proximity is. Indeed, temporal proximity is generally not something taught in schools for healthcare professionals. Moreover, if you submit a complaint anonymously and you are retaliated against, you will not be able to complain that an adverse action was based on your complaint. This is because in submitting it anonymously, you do not have proof that they knew you were the one who complained.

Agency Four

Agency Four provides excellent examples of both retaliation in close temporal proximity and cascading transgressions. Agency Four was a residential treatment program for troubled teens. I have considerable experience in these types of programs. Sadly, I have no experience with a residential treatment program that does not have some history of patients being mistreated or abused in their care, and Agency Four was no exception.

In fact, state investigators frequented Agency Four so often that an office was reserved for them right near the reception area in the main building so that they could conduct their investigations. The leadership team, albeit flawed in many ways, did not ever dissuade anyone from calling in the abuse and they were fastidious about documentation. The facility was well kept and could easily be mistaken for a high-end preparatory school. That said, beyond the façade, substandard care was rife.

The leadership team of Agency Four had a very lax and uncaring attitude toward their staff's behaviors. During my tenure here, this theme would be repeated on multiple occasions. It was always shocking to me because, unlike other places I had worked, Agency Four was an incredibly well-funded nonprofit.

It was not long before I began to correlate that there were increased incidents among residents during certain time periods. I also noted that, during the same time periods, most of the units did not have enough staffing. This became clearly evident in the incident reports that were submitted to me daily by program staff.

As a result of emerging patterns, I became progressively more vocal in management meetings and eventually fell out of favor with some of the senior leadership. This was a big fall because when I was hired, I was advised that I replaced a "big mouth" who, again, was not a "team player." I was quickly viewed as the opposite of her because I was willing to participate more broadly in some of the experiential and outdoor components of the program. I later learned that the woman I replaced was actually a lot like me and was an advocate for better treatment of patients and, therefore, clashed with the leadership team just as I was beginning to do. In addition, I later learned that she was aware of documents my supervisor signed with credentials he did not have.

In leadership meetings I began to bring up my findings about emerging patterns within the units that were causing an unsafe milieu. One of the most pronounced examples was not enough front-line staff. There appeared to be fastidious documentation every few minutes, but not enough staff to effectively supervise the residents. Many smaller incidents were easily missed because of staff being occupied with other essential tasks and there simply not being enough staff to catch incidents before they occurred, or before they evolved into bigger incidents. These smaller incidents became a wealth of cascading trans-gressions that sometimes led to abuse and physical injury to patients. My findings and beliefs were not well received, even when grounded in incident reports and documentation.

The residential director over the front-line staff in Agency Four advised me that they purposely remain short-staffed. He further explained, "When we have more staff they often just stand around and talk." He further rationalized, "They work harder and provide better supervision when it's very busy and not a lot of staff." Of course, I respectfully pushed back on that narrative. Foremost, the incident reports said otherwise. Additionally, I don't think we were ever fully staffed enough to know that all the staff would just stand around and talk and not supervise the residents. Additionally, there are state laws that govern the ratio of staff to residents for most treatment programs. In meeting after meeting, my concerns fell on deaf ears.

Agency Four also took their youth residents on overnight trips that lasted up to a week. These trips were often experiential in nature and were sometimes woven into the clinical programming. As such, the front-line counselors spent the vast majority of the day with the clients. The clinical staff, such as therapists and nurses, did not always stay with the clients but were housed nearby. The educational staff did not usually participate.

As you might surmise, these trips were a cause of contention between staff and administration. Some staff did not want to go on these trips and be pulled from their own families for days at a time. Some staff even presented medical notes to avoid participation. On one trip, a member of the education staff wanted to participate in a week-long trip and the administration permitted it. The educational staff were never required to go on overnight trips with the residents. I believe that the senior leadership was so invested in these trips and wanting to punctuate a point to the resistant staff that they gave little or no thought to why a member of the educational staff would want to attend on her own accord. The decision to allow this staff member to attend would later become a major cascading transgression.

It was subsequently revealed that the member of the educational staff who volunteered to attend this trip had an intimate sexual relationship with a child in the program. Her interest in attending was to continue to advance her intimate relationship with this child. The inappropriate intimacy of this relationship was noticed by a therapist while on the trip and, upon further investigation, it was alleged that this had been an ongoing, progressively escalating, inappropriate relationship.

Similar to other transgressions in Agency Four, the administration was cavalier about these sexual allegations. In fact, the administration's expectation was that the therapist who discovered the abuse, and the alleged abuser, share a hotel room for the night. As you might surmise, the therapist protested and eventually, in spite of the lack of support from administration, ended up not staying in the same room as the alleged abuser. Once we returned to the program's main campus days later, the allegations were investigated by the state. Meanwhile, everything at the agency went on with business as usual and no substantive changes were made.

Over the course of the forthcoming months, Agency Four would take aggressive steps to discharge staff who did not agree with or want to participate in these overnight trips with patients. Some staff left of their own accord as they found other positions. Other staff were terminated.

————

I broach these concepts in this book because it is extremely important to be mindful of the basic precept of constructive discharge (also known as constructive dismissal and constructive termination) and temporal proximity when you are advocating against profane figureheads. It becomes important to have a basic understanding of this practice and to be able to call it out as such. It is always best to contact an employment lawyer to help you determine if your constructive dismissal beliefs are actionable. If not, you might find yourself in constant perdition that goes on and on until you give in and quit. The professional practitioner should make unprofessional supervisors work to terminate them and take the time to gather evidence and proof for the packet so that a legal expert can make a well-informed decision about the potential case.

One may have also noticed that some large healthcare corporations layer their companies and then go through great effort to avoid such vicarious liability. In such configurations, a parent company will try to distance itself from the wrongful actions of an individual facility's leader. The facility leader will also try to distance himself from the wrongful actions of an employee.

They do this to avoid a basic legal precept known as respondeat superior. Lewis and Gardner (2000) explain, "Healthcare facilities are liable for wrongful acts caused by employees' actions in the course and scope of their employment. Because facility administrators have the right to control how work is performed, along with that right goes the responsibility to ensure that the work is properly completed" (Lewis and Gardner, 2000, p. 2). Martucci (1994) affirms, "traditionally, employers have been liable for injury caused by employees' actions in the course and scope of their employment under the doctrine of respondeat superior" (Martucci, 1994, p. 1). Additionally, "courts have held that employers may be liable to victims under a variety of tort theories. The three most common theories alleged are negligent hiring, negligent supervision, and negligent retention" (Martucci, 1994, p. 1).

Chapter Two

Code of Ethics or Code of Silence

The healthcare profession requires individuals to adhere to a certain level of quality and ethics. These ethics are defined by professional licensing boards, state regulations, federal regulations, and various codes of ethics. These entities and codes all foster common themes to provide the highest quality care, and all include standards that advance the basic tenet of doing no harm to patients. That said, so much relies on the good faith of healthcare staff to follow these ethics and laws.

Most, if not all, healthcare professionals subscribe to a formal code of ethics. While a code of ethics is not law, it serves as a guide for how healthcare professionals should conduct themselves in their profession. This is particularly true with how they should most efficaciously render patient care and attempt to define what they should do when care is not efficacious.

In many territories, significant pieces of various codes of ethics can be found grounded in state and federal law. Indeed, there is often a reciprocal relationship between law and codes of ethics. Codes of ethics are often woven into, or pulled from, some parallel legislation. For example, in my case example of Agency One, according to the state licensing board the Social Work Code of Ethics statute (4.07) was grounded in state laws about exploitation of patients and undue influence. Additionally, all licensed healthcare professionals are tied to a licensing board that has rules and regulations, and the vast majority of professionals subscribe to a specific code of ethics for their profession.

Pieces of various codes of ethics that are parallel to state and federal law become actionable and punishable by these laws when broken by the practitioner. Additionally, should practitioners be interviewed by a regulatory agency or attorney, they may be asked, sometimes under oath, if they subscribe to a particular code of ethics. Failure to abide by a specific code of ethics for your profession can impugn your integrity.

Many are familiar with the Physicians Hippocratic Oath. Wecheli, Andreae (1595) believe that this oath stems back to somewhere in the 10th or 11th century. The basic premise of the oath is to do no harm. Commonly phrased, it says, "I will abstain from all intentional wrong-doing and harm" (Wecheli, Andreae, 1595).

The medical code of ethics is perhaps the oldest codes of ethics among the medical professions. The medical code of ethics began as a form of self-regulation among medical doctors. From the onset, it has placed the physician's duty to the patient above all else (Baker & Emanuel 2000).

Additionally, Jonsen and Jameton (1977) describe the ethical concept of nonmaleficence for physicians in four categories that have stood the test of time and remain equally salient today. The four categories, originally espoused in the *Journal of Medicine and Philosophy* in 1977, include: (a) always putting the well-being of the client first by doing no harm; (b) providing adequate and appropriate care for patients; (c) properly assessing the situation including a risk/benefit analysis; and (d) make proper detriment-benefit assessments (Jonsen and Jameton, 1977). These four guidelines should serve as basic tenets for all healthcare employees in determining nonmaleficence.

Additionally, the American Medical Association Medical Code of Ethics continues to serve as a moral code for the medical profession today. According to the American Medical Association (AMA), the Medical Code of Ethics features eleven chapters. The AMA explains, these chapters comprise the "values to which physicians commit themselves as members of the medical profession" (AMA Website). The preamble further adds, "the AMA Principles of Medical Ethics are not laws, but standards of conduct, so too the Opinions in the Code of Medical Ethics are not laws or rules. They are guidance that identifies the essentials of ethical behavior for physicians" (Preamble AMA Principles of Medical Ethics). According to Riddick (2003), in characterizing 2001 changes to the AMA Principles of Medical Ethics, "a physician, while caring for a patient, regards responsibility to the patient as paramount" (Riddick 2003, p. 6).

The American Nurses Association, a leading organization for nursing professionals provides the Nursing Code of

Ethics. The Nursing Code of Ethics features nine provisions. According to the American Nurses Association (2016):

> Provision one characterizes the nurse's obligation to treat each patient with respect and dignity. This provision includes respecting a patient's right to self-determination.

> Provision two addresses the nurse's commitment to the patient and cautions against conflicts of interest. This includes conflicts between client and family, client and agency, and client and nurse.

> Provision three endeavors to provide guidance on patient rights. This includes the nurse's requirement to act on questionable practices promulgated by agencies and others.

> Provision four provides for the accountability of nurses to their patient and others. This includes the responsibility for the nurse's own judgements and actions.

> Provision five addresses the intersection of moral character, integrity, and ethics. This provision addresses the expectation that nurses speak up when situations arise that go against their moral character, integrity, and the code of ethics.

Provision six espouses that nurses must foster and create environments of moral virtues. This includes being part of an environment or moral virtue.

Provision seven speaks to the need to maintain the ethical standards through scholarship and research.

Provision eight recognizes the universal right to health, human rights, and health diplomacy.

Provision nine addresses the role of the nurse in the advancement of social justice.

The provisions of the nursing code of ethics are consistent with the basic canons of all healthcare professionals. These provisions serve as a framework that is grounded in most other codes of ethics and are, perhaps, slightly expanded upon in some others. The belief in the same basic moral compass, however, remains steady throughout the healthcare profession.

The American Psychological Association (APA) Ethical Principles and Psychologists Code of Conduct (2017) shares the basic core principles of the other healthcare professions. The APA Ethical Principles and Psychologist Code of Conduct includes five core principles that are formalized within ten core standards. The core principles include:

Principle A: Beneficence and nonmaleficence
Principle B: Fidelity and responsibility

Principle C: Integrity
Principle D: Justice
Principle E: Respect for people's rights and dignity

The American Psychological Association Code of Conduct is a quite extensive list of standards and principles. These principles share the same basic tenets of the other codes of ethics discussed in this chapter. For example, as noted, Principle A of the American Psychological Association (APA) Code of Conduct deals with beneficence and nonmaleficence. It requires psychologists work to ensure the rights and wellness of all clients and systems and implores that they avoid and do not cause harm to patients. Principle D speaks to justice and implores the protection of patients from unjust practices. Moreover, should ethical situations arise, the code specifically implores "under no circumstances may this standard be used to justify or defend violating human rights" (APA Ethical Principles and Psychologists Code of Conduct 2017) throughout multiple sections of the document.

Similarly, the National Association of Social Workers provides the Social Work Code of Ethics. Much like the codes of ethics for other healthcare professionals, the basic dictum of the Social Work Code of Ethics parallels the concept of doing no harm to patients. In many ways, the current social work code of ethics carries forth the same ethos of other healthcare professions with an emphasis on respect, dignity, and human rights for all clients and patients.

The ethical ethos in social work has evolved considerably

over time. In fact, early discussions of social work ethics actually focused heavily on the morality of the client and then progressively evolved into the ethics and morality of social justice and reform (Reamer 1998). The code of ethics that guides the social work profession today features six core values and 155 ethical standards (Reamer 1998). The six core values of the Social Work Code of Ethics include: service, social justice, dignity and worth of the person, importance of human relationships, integrity, and competence (NASW Code of Ethics). These core values now focus on the best interests of the client and the morality of the social worker.

There are additional codes of ethics worth mentioning as well. The American Counseling Association and the American Association of Marriage and Family Therapists are two additional examples. In fact, most healthcare professionals are governed by some form of a code of ethics for their professions.

The responsibility, often characterized as a duty or obligation, to do no harm to patients and clients is woven throughout the fabric of all healthcare codes of ethics. With so many breaches of these respective codes of ethics galvanizing the healthcare landscape, one must wonder why so many professionals are so discordant with the ethics that govern their profession.

Additionally, when an agency induces healthcare professionals to violate their respective codes of ethics, the burden of this violation falls upon the individual healthcare professional and not the agencies they serve. The healthcare practitioner retains ultimate responsibility for the care they deliver and the actions they perform. This means that the manager who told you to complete some action that violates the code of ethics for your profession is not going to be held liable by your respective licensing board for an action they convinced you to take. Additionally, should an incident be investigated by a regulatory agency, and a complaint filed against a professional license, it will be the violator's problem. As healthcare professionals we are supposed to know better than to comply with an edict from a supervisor or director that could cause harm to a patient and violate our code of ethics. The harm can be direct or indirect, but it always falls upon the professional not to follow an unethical or unlawful order.

The absence of accountability by licensing boards, accrediting bodies, and law enforcement for managers who give unethical directives is quite problematic. This is particularly true when that problematic directive is permitted, or encouraged, by upper management. Indeed, I would argue that this is one of the larger issues confronting the healthcare profession and it leads to substantial abuse, fraud, and general malpractice. Healthcare managers and agencies have the ability to deflect blame to individual practitioners even when they themselves have directed the problematic behavior.

For social workers, this lack of accountability to agencies has become a shifting paradigm. Indeed, the National Association of Social Workers used to be more aggressive in holding agencies accountable. The 1979 Social Work Code of Ethics included standards such as those found in Section IV (2), which articulated: "The social worker should not accept employment or arrange student field placement in an organization which is currently under public sanction by NASW by violating personnel standards, or imposing limitations on or penalties for professional actions on behalf of clients" (Social Work Code of Ethics 1979). This standard was dropped from subsequent versions of the Social Work Code of Ethics. The consequence of this removed standard, albeit unintended, has led to many social workers being left on their own against perditious supervisors and the false propping up of bad healthcare organizations.

Given that common themes in all healthcare workers' code of ethics include actions and beliefs such as quality care, best practices, patient rights to dignity and respect, and an expectation to always do the right thing by patients and to speak up to wrongdoing, it should come as a surprise that many workers in organizations are not above reproach. Sadly, there is ample evidence of healthcare workers bucking their respective codes of ethics, and even law, to support immoral healthcare facilities with slavish fidelity. Clearly, given the wealth of information saturating the media about abuse in institutions, there is a significant gap between ethical theory and praxis among many healthcare practitioners.

While all healthcare educational programs engage students in some ethical discussion, there exists a gap in programs with respect to some of the most serious and taboo boundary issues. This absence is evident throughout the research. Topics such as the healthcare professionals' sexual urges, interests, and sexual actions with patients seem particularly taboo.

More specifically, in a study conducted about nurses who engage in sexual relationships with their patients, more than half of the nurses surveyed said that they had not received education on sexual attraction to patients (Bachmann et. al. 2000). In this same study 17% of male nurses and 11% of female nurses who responded did admit to having had varying degrees of sexual contact with patients in their care (Bachmann et. al. 2000).

Similarly, Gechtman (1989) found that 3.8% of male social workers, and no female social workers, engaged in sexual relationships with clients (Gechtman 1989). Another study of social workers found 1.1 percent of social workers had sex with a former client (Jayaratne et. al. 1997). Between 1969 and 1990 nearly 20 percent (18.5 percent) of malpractice claims against social workers were due to sexual impropriety, making it the second most common malpractice claim (Reamer 1995).

Since this is a book on whistleblowing in healthcare, I was particularly interested to learn about the healthcare workers response to learning about an issue as serious as a colleague having sexual relationships with patients. Only 3.4 percent of social workers formally reported a colleague who was known to be having a sexual relationship with a client (Hutchinson 1991). Similarly, only 8 percent of psychiatrists (Gartrell et al. 1987) and fewer than 20 percent of psychologists (Noel 1988) who were aware of a colleague's sexual misconduct with patients formally reported their colleagues. Considering these statistics, it does not come as a surprise that lesser transgressions in healthcare so often go unreported.

It is my steadfast belief that for the good of the healthcare profession, all practitioners need to become more familiar with how to both protect themselves and how to blow the whistle when necessary. Moreover, when other colleagues act in fealty to an agency or in a manner that protects unethical acts, this leaves the ethical practitioner to be viewed by others with derision. When the practitioner's fealty is to the entity of malpractice and maleficence, they are holding up that fraudulent and false healthcare entity. Simply stated, doing nothing props up bad agencies and makes them look good when they are not. Similarly, rationalizing why you stay in a bad agency for reasons like "I want to stay to protect the patients" also holds up bad agencies. In macro practice, we learn, if the agency and system collapses (in this case from lack of staff) the way is paved for a better agency to come along and do the work.

As many healthcare professionals are aware, this false propping up of bad agencies has paved the way for large and complex health systems to dominate the healthcare market with substandard care and fraud. The micro-practitioner will look to help as many patients as he can within a system, however deeply flawed that system is. The thematic problem with the micro prospective here is that it leads to other patients being mistreated, abused, and even murdered under the umbrella of substandard care. In a healthcare facility with multiple staff, no one practitioner can provide high-quality care to every patient. High-quality care requires a dedicated and committed team of people, who each follow their respective codes of ethics and laws and has the strength of character to do the right thing by patients, always. Moreover, these facilities that deviate from ethics and laws are often entities that spend large sums of money to protect their financial interests above all else.

According to Makary (2016), medical errors are the third largest cause of death in the U.S. and these errors account for more than 250,000 deaths per year. Schindler (2019) joins a growing chorus of healthcare professionals who punctuate the problems leading to the aforementioned patient deaths and cautions against the scapegoating of staff who have been saddled with unrealistic expectations and then scapegoated when something goes wrong.

There exist many commonalities in hospitals that promulgate wrongdoing that leads to substandard care, patient injury, and even patient death. I will broach a few of them here that you may recognize from your own facilities. As noted with Agency Four above, many healthcare facilities operate purposefully understaffed (Schindler 2019, Fry 2018, Cleverley & Harvey 1992, Morley et. al. 2019). Dishonest documentation, unreasonable demands on the workers, and poor hand-off and shift reports are among the problems in healthcare facilities that can lead to poor quality care (Schindler 2019, Norma 2006, Aitamaa et. al. 2010).

Healthcare workers who participate in unethical and unlawful activity often go unpunished. That said, however, one can find instances where workers who participate in, or fail to report, incidents do get punished. Since 2007 the Department of Justice (DOJ) has prosecuted more than 2,000 individuals for their participation in Medicare fraud (Lobosco 2015).

Additionally, in March of 2021, the couple who owned Circle of Hope Girls Ranch (Cedar County, MO) have been charged with more than 100 felonies, including endangering the welfare of a child, statutory sodomy, statutory rape, sexual contact, and child abuse and neglect (Holman 2021). Compounding the tragedy at the Circle of Hope Girls Ranch is the fact that these many incidents were not revealed to authorities by staff at the ranch, but were revealed by the owner's own daughter, who has been exposing the abuse on social media since 2015 (Beneveto 2021); further, documentation exists that suggests that the problems at Circle of Hope have been being reported by victims to authorities for more than ten years (Holman 2021).

The code of silence in healthcare can become life-altering for both practitioner and patient. When you read about incidents at places like Circle of Hope, I hope that you ask yourself, "Where were the staff who let this go on? Why didn't anyone blow the whistle on systemic abuse that was so pervasive over a ten-year period?" Certainly, the healthcare worker does not see these competing issues as dilemmatic, as they are not equally undesirable alternatives. Yet, in case after case, the healthcare worker struggles with this moral dilemma and maintains the code of silence. If, as healthcare workers, we do not hold ourselves to our respective codes of ethics, they will degenerate into mere theoretical postulations.

Chapter Three

Healthcare Worker Versus Patient: Their Wellbeing or Yours

When a healthcare worker knows that the outcome of blowing the whistle and advocating for patients is likely to result in some form of adverse action, this worker is put in a conflicting paradigm. The literature reveals that some nurses, for example, report that they do not come forward and report witnessed unethical behavior due to fear of retaliation by administration and coworkers (Mansbach & Bachner, 2010).

This fear of retaliation becomes particularly true in cases such as those illustrated in my case example of Agency One, where people have borne witness to adverse actions that happened to others who spoke up. Indeed, watching 18 directors forced out in 17 months, as was the case in Agency One, could truly give pause to some of the best advocates. Profane figureheads will see any form of advocacy as a betrayal and the most abject treachery. This type of leader is generally too short-sighted and does not possess the skill set to correlate the facts that doing the right thing leads to better patient care, which almost always ultimately leads to more clients and higher profits. Profane figureheads often force the healthcare practitioner into a false choice between moral distress or moral courage.

Jameton (1993) characterizes moral distress as feelings that equate to a painful psychological imbalance or disequilibrium that arises when one knows the right thing to do, but institutional constraints make it nearly impossible to do the right thing. Schluter et al. (2008) describes the moral distress as arising from an awareness of three basic areas: poor-quality care, unsuccessful advocacy, and unrealistic hope. Maluwa et. al. (2012) further describes causes of moral distress to include: "shortage of staff, violating regulations in order to protect patients, being forced to accept disrespect, lack of resources, behavior of colleagues and mismanagement by superiors and bosses" (Maluwa et. al. 2012, p. 199).

Kidder (2005), an ethicist who founded the Institute for Global Ethics, describes five basic characteristics of individuals with high moral courage. These five principles include:

1. greater confidence in principles than personalities
2. high tolerance for ambiguity, exposure, and personal loss
3. acceptance of deferred gratification and simple rewards
4. independence of thought
5. formidable persistence and determination. (Kidder 2005 p.18)

Similarly, Bahnaman (2009) describes moral courage as possessing seven specific virtues: wisdom, care, respectfulness, trustworthiness, justice, courage, and integrity. Day (2007) characterizes moral courage as a postulation vital for people to take hold of, and to fully support, the ethical responsibilities critical to professional values. Further, "Moral courage is a highly esteemed trait displayed by individuals who, despite adversity and personal risk, decide to act upon their ethical values to help others during difficult ethical dilemmas" (Murray 2010, p. 2). Some consider moral courage to be the apex of ethical behavior because it requires a steadfast commitment to fundamental ethical principles despite many obvious risks. Indeed, morally courageous individuals willingly face adversity, confront unparalleled uncertainties, and remain steadfast in their ethics and resolve (Iseminger 2010, LaSala & Bjarnason 2010, Clancy 2003, Kidder 2005, Peake 2006).

Irreverent leaders become quite adept at forcing Practitioners into the paradigm of moral distress versus moral courage. Such figureheads become fixated on profits over patient care and are too short-sighted to see how their behaviors and actions hinder both. Such leaders have been quite expert at reducing healthcare workers to chattel. Pressure to stay in line, whistleblower retaliation, and termination of those who dare speak up are all tools regularly used to keep workers in line.

Whistleblower retaliation comes in many forms. According to the United States' Project on Government Oversight, typical forms of retaliation include (Project on Government Oversight, 2005):

- Taking away job duties so that the employee is marginalized.
- Taking away an employee's national security clearance so that he or she is
- effectively fired.
- Blacklisting an employee so that he or she is unable to find gainful employment.
- Conducting retaliatory investigations in order to divert attention from the waste, fraud, or abuse the whistleblower is trying to expose.
- Questioning a whistleblower's mental health, professional competence, or
- honesty.
- Setting the whistleblower up by giving impossible assignments or seeking to
- entrap him or her.
- Reassigning or relocating an employee so he or she is unable to do the job.

Although the aforementioned speaks directly to employees of government entities, similar retaliatory methods apply in the public sector as well. As noted, similar protections from these retaliatory actions do not always apply to private-sector whistleblowers. Nonetheless, the points serve to help define actions an employer may take against you for reporting misconduct.

Additionally, so much has been written about the whistleblower with respect to the retaliation and adverse actions that he or she faces. The adverse actions and the consequences that result from retaliatory actions are real and can often extend beyond the whistleblower's current employer. For example, whistleblower cases sometimes enter the public domain through inspection reports, court filings, and media stories.

The attention garnered from whistleblowing can then become problematic for future employment. It is important to remain cognizant of the possible long-term consequences of blowing the whistle and to also, simultaneously, realize that it is possible to reinvent yourself after. Whistleblowing does not have to be the career ending, long-term depression-inducing, quandary that is often portrayed in articles and texts. That said, it would be remiss to ignore the profound impact whistleblowing can have on the healthcare professional who decides to speak up against wrongdoing. Indeed, the consequences of whistleblowing can be wide ranging. The consequences often begin in the workplace and then permeate the whistleblower's personal life and can have a deleterious effect on their overall wellbeing.

In the workplace, whistleblowers are often viewed by colleagues as "troublemakers" and are often treated with derision. Johnstone (2004) describes how colleagues often take a defensive stance against the whistleblower and frame them as a troublemaker. This takes a toll on emotional health as well. In a qualitative study including 18 nurses, Jackson et. al. (2010) found that whistleblowing had an incredible negative and prodigious effect on our relationships with colleagues. K. Kenny et. al (2018, p. 812) characterize the work place retaliation whistleblowers received as "being cast outside of the organization for performing one's duty and/or protecting the public interest, under conditions of acute mental strain" and suggest that it "represents a powerful form of normative violence exercised by organizations over individuals who dissent" (K. Kenny et al. 2018, p.812).

A study completed by Rothschild & Miethe (1999, p. 120) illuminates the workplace consequences of blowing the whistle. Indeed, Rothschild & Miethe (1999) found that whistleblowers experienced the following forms of retaliation from their employer or coworkers as a result of their disclosures:

- lost their job or were forced to retire.
- received negative job performance evaluations.
- had work more closely monitored by supervisors.
- were criticized or avoided by coworkers.
- were blacklisted from getting another job in their field.

Additionally, many whistleblowers eventually end up being forced out or terminated from their positions. Alford (2001) sums up this retaliation and characterizes the whistleblower's fate as "sacrificed as a lesson to others in the group, so they will see the price of acting as an ethical individual who remembers that he or she belongs to the world" (Alford 2001, p. 125).

Moreover, qualitative research by Peters et. al. (2011) characterizes the long-term effects of whistleblowing. The Peters et. al. research found that, even a year after blowing the whistle, whistleblowers were still experiencing flashbacks, intrusive thoughts and incapacitating emotions. The albeit unintended long-term effects impeded the whistleblowers capacity to work and meaningfully engage activities or life with their families (Peters et. al. 2011, p.8).

Greaves and McGlone (2012) characterize their review of consequences to whistleblowers and describe whistleblowers as experiencing weight fluctuations and problems with sleep disturbance. Some whistleblowers who were living alone stopped looking after themselves and experienced varying degrees of depression. Additionally, the ostracism and false performance reporting had made people doubt themselves, describing situations where they felt that they were treated "like a leper." They felt no one would want to be around them and they express the desire to disappear (Greaves and McGlone, 2012, p. 261). Similarly, Rothschild & Miethe (1999) found that the majority of whistleblowers suffered "severe depression or anxiety…feelings of isolation or powerlessness…distrust of others…declining physical health…severe financial decline and problems with family relations" (Rothschild and Miethe, 1999, p. 121). Whistleblowers often experience physical symptoms as well. These physical symptoms can include: lack of energy, nervous system and immune system problems, respiratory and cardiac symptoms, and digestive system problems (McDonald & Ahern 2002).

In my own experience, you are likely to face consequences the very minute you question any policy, procedure, or action that you find questionable. You will hear trigger encouragement/discouragement phrases like "you have to understand these are very difficult patients and things happen" or you are exhorted to be a "team player." You may even be encouraged to write, and rewrite, your report of an incident so that it is written in a way that is favorable. The favorable report constitutes deference to the agency and fealty to the chief executive, at the expense of both factual accuracy and the patient.

Despite the aforementioned potential consequences, the whistleblower remains an important tool to protect patients against the impact substandard care and abuse has on patients' lives. Indeed, for many whistleblowers the ramifications of bankrupting their own moral fortitude and the consequences to patients far exceed the consequences to self. For many patients, healthcare programs with pernicious leaders equate to institutional practice that is harmful and potentially deadly. For many healthcare professionals the neglect and abuse to patients, as a consequence of not speaking up, is not even an option because it comes into conflict with their moral compass.

Patient neglect is commonly defined as "the failure of a designated caregiver to meet the needs of a dependent" (Lachs, 1995, p. 437). In a review of literature on patient neglect in healthcare settings, Reader & Gillespie (2013) found "neglect to be quite a subjective construct, and this partially explains why neglect and error can become confused" (Reader & Gillespie, 2013, p. 8). Further, "qualitative studies of patient neglect frequently take the perspectives of both caregivers and patients in trying to understand why poor care occurs" (Reader & Gillespie, 2013, p. 8). Thematic in all healthcare codes of ethics is the steadfast belief in doing no harm, also known as nonmaleficence, to patients.

Harm can be broadly defined to include physical, emotional, and psychological harm, as well as violations of human rights (Beauchamp & Childress, 2013).

In some studies, nurses working in environments where they are short-staffed, found situations where good patients were often rewarded with prompt care and more difficult patients deliberately delayed care as nurses struggled to meet the needs of all patients (Khalil 2009). Reader & Gillespie (2013) describe these work environments: "under-resourcing (e.g. personnel or materials) which results in too many patients to care for, too many tasks to perform, constantly changing workloads, and burgeoning bureaucracy" (Reader & Gillespie, 2013, p. 10).

Abuse in residential treatment facilities is, sadly, an occurrence more common than most people may realize. This is particularly true in facilities that serve the youth population. In fact, one study on child sexual abuse in residential treatment found, "A child in a residential home is 6 times more likely to be assessed and reported by a pediatrician for physical or sexual abuse than a child in the general population" (Hobbs et. al 1999 p. 8).

There is not a lot of research that takes an in-depth look at abuse that specifically occurred in residential treatment programs or on the long-term impact of children being abused in such programs. Others have also noted that there is a lack of reliable research and a lack of data on patient abuse in institutions (Sandrum 2006) and even difficulty defining what constitutes abuse in institutions (Hirst 2002). This is likely because, if we examine these systems honestly, we will find that they are ineffective in their stated missions. This discovery would likely turn the troubled-teen industry upside down.

Similarly, there is also a dearth of information regarding the effectiveness of residential treatment programs in improving the lives of youth. Simply, we are likely to find out that youth being discharged from these programs are the same or possibly worse off than they were before they entered the programs. Many of them exit with what are now compounded – from home and from their time in the program – histories of trauma and abuse (Hummer et. al. 2010). Finding these child and teen industry institutions ineffective would serve to illustrate that the problems plaguing the industry are deeply thematic and profoundly irremediable. In fact, for some of us, the problems facing this industry are trite and ignominious. Yet others, turn a blind eye, become taciturn, or simply give up, finding these institutions indomitable. Some researchers have questioned if residential treatment programs have more drawbacks than they do advantages (Major 2018, p. 2).

Despite a serious lack of peer-reviewed research articles, actual news stories of children being abused in residential treatment centers abound and have become increasingly polarized throughout the mainstream media. In many cases, the abused are speaking up where multiple staff have failed to. In fact, there are so many individual stories about abuse in institutions that it is enough fodder for a different book just on the topic of institutional abuse alone. For the purposes of punctuating the consequences of a healthcare worker acting obsequious, I will give attention to some major stories in this chapter.

A CNN story in 2014 revealed more than a dozen allegations of child abuse, including a sustained pattern of long-term abuse, in a Colorado treatment facility, Adolescent and Family Institute of Colorado. The article revealed "15 civil suits and some two dozen complaints to state regulators" and adds "the allegations include verbal and sexual abuse, unauthorized discontinuance of psychotropic medication and fraud" (Cabrara and Weisfeldt, 2014). This story also punctuates the concerns outlined in chapter four about the thematic failures of state and federal agencies to protect patients in healthcare settings. Indeed, the news story explains, "Colorado public records obtained by CNN detail similar complaints and other alleged abuses that date back to the mid-1980s"(Cabrara and Weisfeldt, 2014). Further, CNN obtained hundreds of pages of records that show state regulators were made aware of the problems at AFIC and the records illustrate how the regulators did investigate. Yet the regulators and investigators have said the allegations "could not be confirmed" (Cabrara and Weisfeldt, 2014). According to the *Denver Post*, AFIC was "accredited by The Joint Commission on Accreditation of Health Care Organizations (now, The Joint Commission) since 1984 and licensed by the Department of Human Services' Child Care Division and the Division of Behavioral Health's mental-health office" (Mitchell, 2012). AFIC is now closed.

CRC Health Group touted itself as a leading provider of mental health services for children, adolescents, and adults. CRC owned more than 100 facilities across the U.S. CRC Health group represented a group of healthcare facilities plagued with substandard care lawsuits and allegations of patient abuse and neglect. Levine (2012) reports that some of the incidents include "a history of abuse allegations, including at least three lawsuits, and two known patient deaths" in their Aspen Education Group programs. Levine (2012) further characterizes an affidavit by a physician, who frequently referred patients to CRC's Youth Care programs, accusing sexual assault of a female student and what he characterized as "brutish punishment and isolation" of students. The allegations further add, "The girl was later duct-taped and restrained by staff after writing complaints about abusive staff conduct to management." The incidents were reported to state regulators and the local county sheriff in 2004 and later became part of a lawsuit (Levine 2012).

According to Levine (2012) the problems at CRC extended into their adult programs as well. According to reports, in January of 2012 staff at Sierra Tucson (Arizona) failed to follow 1:1 order on a 71-year-old suicidal patient. The patient subsequently went missing for two weeks before he was eventually found dead on the grounds. Upon investigation of the incident, Arizona regulators "found 42 major violations [and] the center was put on one-year probation" (Levine, 2012).

The problems within the CRC system of care extended throughout the country. The summary of just some of the major incidents reported by Levine (2012) include:

- In 2010, CRC's New Life Lodge (Burns, TN) faced two wrongful death suits and other complaints throughout the years. At one point the state of Tennessee slowed admissions to New Life Lodge.

- In 2009, State investigators found "nine cases of abuse and neglect at Mount Bachelor Academy in central Oregon, including incidents of "sexualized role play," in which young patients were allegedly forced to do sexually provocative dances during their therapy sessions (Levine 2012).
- At SageWalk Wilderness School (OR) a 16-year-old boy died of heatstroke (Levine 2012).

Additionally, the Department of Justice has investigated CRC Health Group for criminal fraud. According to an article in Behavioral Healthcare Executive, CRC Health Group (CRC) will pay $9.25 million to the federal government, as well as the State of Tennessee, to settle allegations surrounding substandard care and the submission of false claims that they submitted on behalf of Medicaid patients at their facility in Burns, TN (Brys, 2014).

CRC facilities have enjoyed accreditation by The Joint Commission and are licensed by their respective states of operation. CRC Health Group was acquired by Acadia Healthcare in 2014 (PR Newswire, NY).

In 2019, the U.S. Department of Justice announced a $17 million healthcare fraud settlement with Acadia Healthcare. The May 6, 2019, press release, from the U.S. Attorney's Office of the Southern District of West Virginia, characterizes a settlement reached after allegations of criminal fraud in Acadia's West Virginia CRC Health, L.L.C. ("CRC") drug treatment centers throughout West Virginia.

Acadia Healthcare now reports owning more than 500 facilities across the country. The problems plaguing Acadia facilities are multifarious and appear to be steeped in a corporate culture of fraud and abuse enabled by taciturn staff. Some of the problems at Acadia's facilities include:

- A December 6, 2019, police raid of Acadia's Lakeview Behavioral Health (Gwinnett County, GA). According to news reports, more than 50 officers raided the facility in an effort to gather information on 46 claims of patient neglect abuse. Allegations include a patient being put in a freezer for so long that he lost a toe and incidents of both physical and sexual abuse. (VerHelst, 2019). Lakeview Behavioral Health is accredited by The Joint Commission and is licensed by the state of Georgia.
- Acadia's North Tampa Behavioral Hospital (Wesley Chapel, FL) has been plagued with systemic problems. In 2019, the *Tampa Bay Times* did an exposé on the Wesley Chapel facility and highlighted several problems. Foremost, the expose provided great detail about how the facility exploited the Florida Baker Act laws to increase hospital profits and viability by holding patient's

hostage, through Baker Act loopholes, in their facility. The facility has suffered other problems as well. According to the article, "since 2014, it [North Tampa Behavioral Hospital] has been cited 72 times for unsafe conditions and code violations, more than all but one other psychiatric hospital in Florida" (Bedi 2019). Further, inspectors have reported "unqualified and undertrained staff members" who put patients in danger and violated their human rights (Bedi 2019). The article also broaches issues of security at the facility, citing cases where at least six people who were to be committed to secured units under the Baker Act have been able to elope from the facility; one patient did so utilizing a staff key card (Bedi, 2019). In 2016, two suicidal patients were able to hang themselves; fortunately, both did survive. In 2018, two allegations of sexual assault occurred (Bedi, 2019). North Tampa Behavioral Hospital is accredited by The Joint Commission and is licensed by the state of Florida.

- Timberline Knolls, Acadia Healthcare's facility in Lemont (IL), touts itself as a premier treatment center for women. According to the *Chicago Tribune*, six women who were patients at Timberline Knolls alleged sexual assault by staff. The article further reports "patients were subjected to rape, forced oral sex, digital penetration and fondling beneath their clothes" (Jackson 2019). In total, 62 felony charges were filed against a staff member at Timberline Knolls. Worse, as the article reports, "the abuse allegations began to surface last summer, but Timberline officials waited at least three weeks to contact law enforcement, police reports show" (Jackson 2019). According to police call records, "police responded to 14 allegations of patient-on-patient sex crimes or batteries at the facility last year, compared with a total of 12 such cases in the previous three years. Meanwhile, Timberline reported 10 missing persons or runaways to Lemont police in 2018, compared with seven reports total in the previous three years" (Jackson 2019). Timberline Knolls is accredited by The Joint Commission and is licensed by the state of Illinois.

- Acadia's Park Royal Hospital (Fort Myers, FL) is another Acadia Healthcare facility plagued with an extensive history of abhorrent problems. In 2014 a staff member at Park Royal Hospital fabricated records indicating that he had completed 15-minute checks on a patient when the staff member did not. The patient died in the hospital (Carpenter 2016). According to *Naples News*, "Six weeks before [a patient's death], [another] patient followed a staff member out through a locked door. The patient's absence wasn't discovered for 2 hours

and 20 minutes" (Carpenter 2016). According to
the article, the patient death came approximately
one year after "a nonmedical staff member pleaded
guilty to sexual assault charges and received five
years in prison" (Carpenter 2016). According to
the article in *Naples News*, 12 women have sued
the facility. According to the *Tampa Bay Times*,
Park Royal "has paid more than $3 million in
settlements to eight former patients who said they
had been sexually abused by an employee" and
"Park Royal is the only Florida psychiatric hospital
with more citations than North Tampa Behavioral. It has been cited by state regulators more than
100 times since 2014" (Bedi 2019). Park Royal
Hospital and North Tampa Behavioral Health are
both managed by Acadia Healthcare. Both facilities are accredited by The Joint Commission and
remain licensed by the state of Florida.

Sadly, there is no government entity that thoroughly and
comprehensively tracks the allegations of abuse in residential
treatment centers. This makes it difficult to recognize the nature
and depth of abuse in institutions and parallels the problem of
the lack of research on this issue. NBC News reported that
the Government Accountability Office (GAO) has data from
more than 30 states in which more than 1,500 staff members
were accused of abuse in residential programs; these data were
collected during a one-year period (Nadi et. al. 2013).

Fraud and abuse are so ubiquitous throughout healthcare that it is impossible to ignore the tacit, and sometimes overt, role of healthcare workers. Sometimes this fraud and patient abuse is pernicious and begins with cascading transgressions, while at other times it is more overt, yet it is still covered up.

AGENCY TWO

Cascading transgressions and abuse were widespread throughout all levels of Agency Two. In so many instances, teams of people could have responsibly discharged their fiduciary responsibilities to provide better care to the patients, but pestilent leadership ran rampant throughout the agency.

In one example of a cascading transgression in Agency Two, I saw an incident report written to justify a restraint placed on a combative patient and who spit on a staff member. The patient had become combative and was put into a hold for the safety of everyone on the unit. What the report failed to mention, however, was that the staff member spit back into the patient's face. This omission is a cascading transgression. Failure to note the spitting on the patient will lead to that staff member's not being trained properly, disciplined, or terminated. Any staff member who spits on a patient really does not possess the disposition to work in a healthcare setting (or probably any setting) and it is probably only a matter of time before he seriously physically injures a patient. Yet in multiple instances in Agency Two, I witnessed enticement to leave salient things out of reports, and you probably have in other agencies too. For the sake of quality patient care, and the practitioners' moral compass, these types of transgressions cannot continue to be tenable.

Moreover, the consequences of blowing this whistle were fatal at Agency Two. Staff members spoke frequently about other staff members who had tried to speak up and were abruptly terminated. Consistent with the literature, the Trifecta of Evil and Abuse (the three staff members who enabled wrongdoing) that ran Agency Two made every effort to marginalize those who spoke up. Indeed, Ferree & Smith (1979) describe the treatment of whistleblowers as "membership in a devalued group and may correspond to what is generally understood as 'minority status' in our society" (Ferree & Smith, 1979, p. 87). Silencing those who speak up, even if by termination, was top priority for the Trifecta.

In this agency, I did not, however, experience the lack of support from my direct colleagues that is highlighted throughout a lot of the literature. Many of my colleagues tried to speak up, were shot down, and then got in line because others who attempted to go further were fired. This isn't to say everyone in Agency Two was aligned; there were factions. Many of us had multiple meetings behind closed doors discussing what could be done about the abusive staff and leadership at this facility. Many felt powerless and did not know what to do or how to activate other external systems effectively. Worse, many of the staff that had been there a while saw the external systems repeatedly fail to effectively address the problems that plagued this facility.

At Agency Two, there seemed to be a profound understanding

that this abhorrent leadership had led to significant harm to patients, but there remained considerable debate among colleagues about what should be done and how. In one meeting with some managers and other therapists, we debated and questioned: Do you believe in speaking up until the problem is fixed and you probably get fired, or do you believe that you should do your best to stay as long as possible to protect the patients you can protect? Indeed, I did witness incidents where the "good people" would intervene, in one particular incident or another, on the bad staff to prevent immediate harm to a patient.

———

It is my belief, however, that convincing yourself to stay to protect a few is deeply flawed self-talk to justify failing to act decisively and to justify a desire to keep a job regardless of the type of agency in which you are employed. The macro practitioner understands that good people staying in bad agencies only props the agency up with a false sense of quality. I entered the healthcare field to improve lives, not to falsely prop up an agency that damages lives.

The long-term effects of being abused in a facility can be prolonged and profound. As healthcare professionals, it is our fiduciary responsibility to ensure these types of abuses do not continue to happen.

The long-term impact of abuse is a well-studied topic. There is a direct correlation between physical abuse and sexual abuse in childhood with a lifelong battle with anxiety, depression, sleep disturbance, suicide, substance abuse, sexual risk behaviors, and also an increased prevalence of medical problems (Chen et.al. 2010, Greenwood et. al. 1990, Jeremy et. al. 2003, Cheasty et. al. 1998, Abdala et. al. 2016, Wise et. al. 2001). Emotional abuse, albeit sometimes more subtle, can often lead to lifelong problems with fear and rejection (Maciejewski & Mazure 2006).

I will close out this chapter by giving voice to a boy who was repeatedly abused in an institution. Allen Knoll, in his book *Surviving Bethel: A True Story*, wrote of his experiences at the notorious Bethel Baptist Boys Academy and the long-term negative impact it has had on his life. Sadly, his story is far too common among programs across the country. Now an adult, Allen explains that his time at Bethel "left me traumatized and broken" (Knoll 2018, p. 123). He further explains:

> "The psychological damage was and is severe. It has been 17 years since I escaped the hell of Bethel and the truth is, I never really escaped Bethel. It follows me every day. It wakes me up regularly in the form of nightmares. It haunts me in my day-to-day life and it seems to have stolen my personal happiness. All these years later, as a young adult, I am still battling...It is a fight that will probably never end...As an adult it is torture for me to think about what could have been...I suffered more with the loss of my family and of my childhood. I can never replace those things and it is completely overwhelming to think about" (Knoll 2018, p. 123).

Chapter Four

Accomplices and Imposters

All the aforementioned fraud, abuse, and harm to patients would be far less possible, if not impossible, if healthcare organizations did not have accomplices and imposters. Accomplices and imposters are the anodyne people of the healthcare facility. Accomplices and imposters are also those individuals who actively perpetuate the problems. They have no discernable commitment to their codes of ethics, or to the law, and act simply to keep their own jobs. Both accomplices and imposters are equally bad for the safety and treatment of the patients throughout our nation's healthcare organizations.

Hospitals and other healthcare organizations also employ people to help protect the company at all costs. In larger systems this is accomplished through a variety of positions that are truly only geared toward protection of the company and the facilities they manage. All healthcare systems accomplish this is through use of people with titles like Risk Managers, Corporate Compliance Officers, Ethics Officers, and similar titles. Healthcare facilities also accomplish this self-protection through other mechanisms like corporate compliance hotlines.

The risk managers' stated purpose may be to protect patients, but in many cases their real existence is only for the tacit, and sometimes not so tacit, goal of protecting the agency. Sometimes, protecting the agency and the patient's interests align and sometimes they do not. Risk managers are often put in a dilemma between the interest of the corporation and the interests of the government regulators (Haiko et. al. 2019). Risk managers, corporate compliance officers, and ethics officers rarely act independently of the corporation they represent and often report directly to the agency administration. These competing interests usually put the ethicist in fidelity with the meritocracy they report to. In fact, Hoffman, et. al. (2008) believes that individuals in these positions should be able to conduct their work independently of agency administration, but they rarely do. Moreover, in healthcare settings, all employees should be considered risk managers (Sheffer 2018). These roles being incorporated into the agency with a chain of command, in which they report to agency administration, consistently serves to make them loyal to administration and not laws, regulations, or patients.

Agency Two

Agency Two is a great example of how the interests of the patients were often secondary to the interests of the agency. That is, the agency's interest of keeping the census up and the profits high. For any practitioner to penetrate the administration of this agency they must have an indefatigable commitment to human rights.

In Agency Two, I frequently referred to the Risk Manager, the Director of Nursing, and the Chief Executive Officer as the Trifecta of Abuse or the Trifecta of Evil. Nothing could have halted the sheer pestilence of these three individuals. When an improper incident occurred, these three acted in concert to protect the agency and often the offending staff member(s) above all else. When someone attempted to speak up, these three acted unitedly to stifle anyone who dared speak up to make the agency safer and better. There was little to no interest in holding wrongdoers accountable for their actions. As such, the offending staff members supported the Trifecta with slavish fidelity and became increasingly emboldened in their wrongdoing.

Under the leadership of the Trifecta of Abuse, Agency Two was cited by state regulators for failing to follow mandated reporting responsibilities for allegations of patient abuse on multiple occasions. Incidents of alleged abuse were frequently not called into the state's abuse reporting hotline. The Trifecta was also responsible for lost documentation, lost video footage, and generally covering up any evidence of abuse to patients in an effort to protect disreputable staff and the facility.

In fact, the Trifecta's actions were so bold that a watchdog agency filed a licensing board complaint against the Director of Nursing for her role in this complicity. The licensing board complaint utilized information found in multiple state investigative reports, and the citations found in those reports, which identified the nursing department as complicit in the failure to report allegations of patient abuse, failure to take actions to prevent the same, and other violations of human rights.

In follow up of therapists at the agency continuing to report allegations of abuse to the state abuse hotline as required, the CEO directed the Risk Manager to meet with us. In this meeting we were advised that critical incidents and allegations of abuse should not be documented in the patient record. They should be documented, she explained, on incident reports that were sent to corporate because the patients' medical record is "discoverable" in court. In other words, they wanted allegations patients made about abuse to disappear into corporate head-quarters with no trace of them on site at the physical location of the facility.

———

Agency Three

Another interaction with a risk manager whose values aligned more with the agency than the patients came when I was working in a residential treatment program, Agency Three. I was a director in this agency and, in this role, I was senior to all the front-line staff. The agency had a prior history of physical and sexual abuse of patients in their care. They also had a history of underreporting allegations of abuse by patients where the abuse was allegedly perpetrated by staff. The state the agency operated in was frustrated with the agency and both licensing and disability rights had a tenuous relationship with the agency as a result of their failure to report incidents properly. I was brought in as part of a turnaround team under a new CEO who I knew did things the right way.

Shortly into my stint in this treatment program, there was a serious incident involving a youth in the program. The agency had a lobby area near the units where there was an enclosed nursing station. The station was encased in clear polycarbonate. Upon being told by the nursing staff that a youth had been taken to the hospital for a cut on his head that resulted from a staff restraint that had occurred by the nurses' station, I immediately began review of the video footage from the cameras in that area.

Upon video review of the incident, I witnessed a youth using his fists to bang on the polycarbonate of the nurse's station. I imagine this was quite frustrating for the nurses who did their best, for some reason, to ignore the youth. Shortly after the incident began, I saw one staff member enter the area to intervene. The staff member grabbed the youth by his arms and then spun the kid around and tried to place him on the floor in a physical hold. The area was not clear of furniture and the youth hit his head on the corner of a table on the way down to the ground resulting in a gash on his head that required medical attention outside the facility. I was initially contacted because a patient was sent to the hospital and, in my leadership role, I was to be alerted of such incidents.

It is my hope that healthcare workers who read this realize several salient factors. Foremost, why didn't the nurses just ask the patient what was wrong? This may have avoided the incident entirely. Additionally, I hope people realize that there is no imminent threat of harm when a person bangs his hands on polycarbonate. It's a substance used in many healthcare facilities, particularly psychiatric units, because it is incredibly difficult to break. Additionally, it does not shatter like glass. Further, the staff member attempted to perform a physical hold by himself, which was against company policy, it is not how we trained him on how to do a hold and performing a hold in this situation should have been counterintuitive. The hold was unnecessary, against policy, and performed incorrectly.

After reviewing the incident on camera, I made a prompt decision to terminate this staff member. It remains my steadfast belief that this incident constituted child abuse. Within an hour or two, I wrote the firing document, had it approved by the CEO, had it signed off on by human resources (HR), created a copy of the video for the state investigators, called the incident into the state abuse hotline, and terminated the staff. The staff member was gone within an hour or two.

The Risk Manager, however, spent three days investigating this incident. She was not apprised he was fired; perhaps that was my fault, as I believed this was an HR function. Over the course of three days, the risk manager gathered witness statements from the staff members, friends and colleagues, worked on additional incident reports, and I believe did her best to justify keeping the staff member. Three days later, when she provided the results of her investigation to me, I let her know the staff member was terminated. Her response to me was, "Oh

I guess there is a new way of doing things now." Indeed, there was a new and less abusive way of doing things.

Within very close proximity of the aforementioned incident, in Agency Three, there was a fire set by a patient on one of the units. Upon review of camera footage that day it became apparent that the patient planned the fire throughout the day and spent hours during the morning routine amassing all the supplies to set this fire. Many of the items were contraband, but the staff were not properly supervising the patients and the fire was the culminating incident. The cascading transgressions began with laxed supervision on the unit in a facility that touts 24/7 supervision of residents. The fire damaged a full patient room and caused the unit to be closed down for over a month. Several staff were terminated as a result of this incident because their lack of supervision put patients and staff at risk.

———

Throughout all my professional experiences spanning multiple decades, I have never worked in a facility that did not have at least one of the following: problematic staff or incidents of substandard care. Both problematic staff and incidents of substandard care all equate to patient abuse, neglect, and even death. I would find it hard to believe any healthcare worker who claims he or she never witnessed, or became familiar with, something wrong at their agency. The key difference is that some agencies are looking to clean things up and others are looking to cover things up. Again, in the less ethical agencies, you will notice reports written to protect the agency that will omit details because "they make people look bad." I have been unfortunate to have worked for multiple unethical agencies, and fortunate enough to work for some that are willing to clean things up.

In Agency Three, with the youth who was thrown into a table and the staff who was subsequently fired, I worked for a fantastic CEO who was strength-based and solution-focused. He was intolerant of patient abuse and allowed prompt termination of staff who did not have the patient's best interest in mind, always. I began working at this agency in December, and by the end of January I fired, with his blessing, 13 people in my department in an effort to improve the efficacy of the treatment provided within the agency.

Many of the staff I terminated were fired for failing to supervise patients and/or for being too verbally and physically aggressive with patients, meaning, they were quick to rationalize putting patients in physical holds and were not on-board with the practice of trauma-informed care. Indeed, the literature on the damage done by physical holds is quite extensive and impacts both staff and patients. Staff and patients, both of whom frequently get injured during physical holds. Straut (2010) did a review of qualitative studies done on patient restraints in various healthcare settings. Thematic in the research examined, patients described their restraint experiences as dehumanizing and causing broken spirits, physical and mental exhaustion, feelings of hopelessness and helplessness, being punished unnecessarily, and being abused (Straut 2010).

In most of the cases at Agency Three, the incidents were not classified as abuse by external agencies, but the staff members were terminated anyway. The reasons were because I understand the concept of cascading transgressions and we were trying to create a team of trauma informed staff who avoid putting patients through the trauma of physical holds. I never wanted to be employed in an agency where patients were abused and will certainly never participate in minimizing it or covering it up.

It is fortunate when you work for a director and agency that protects patients at all costs, even if the facts of a situation make an agency look bad or could get them terminated. Sadly, good leaders often do not last. In some agencies, you will find profane figureheads with mock morals and ethics promulgating substandard care and an environment of thematic and cascading transgressions. It does not matter if your participation is overt, it will signal tacit approval of the wrongdoing.

Let us also not delude ourselves into thinking that external constituencies are not aware of an agency's shortcomings. Healthcare professionals who hold up substandard facilities will eventually find they have eroded their credibility because they appear ostensibly on board with the agency's malfeasance and substandard care. If you have not found this already, you will eventually find that referring agencies are often aware of the substandard care in an agency but find themselves with no other viable referral options. As such, your professional reputation will become aligned with the substandard care your agency provides.

Corporate Compliance & Corporate Coverup

The corporate compliance department and corporate compliance hotline is one such way I have witnessed the loyalty of corporate headquarters to a facility over the patients in that facility. As many healthcare workers who work in corporations that own multiple facilities know, there is often a corporate compliance line that an employee can call and report when they witness substandard patient care. The line is managed by the parent corporation, so it is not reporting anything outside the corporation. Usually, the line is promised to be free of adverse consequences to employees who report problems at any given facility. Trust the anonymity and confidentiality at your own peril.

In most corporations that I have worked for, however, the corporate compliance line is not remotely what they depict it to be. If an incident reported is serious enough, it warrants a visit from corporate. One colleague of mine aptly referred to these corporate teams as the Voltaire. As you may already be aware, these are teams of people who come in, usually and suits and almost always with laptops, and they act to aggressively clean up and bury any mess. The Voltaire do so under the guise that they are there to take the issue seriously, but that is simply untrue. In most cases I have experienced, their actions tell a much different story.

This corporate brigand exists to help protect the agency, not the patients. They clean up any mess that leaves the agency vulnerable to outside attacks such as investigations and lawsuits. They are there to ensure the agency is protected at all costs and to help facilitate building the case against the person who called in the first place and to minimize consequences to the company by whatever means necessary. Rest assured, even if you are able to get information to corporate compliance anonymously, the behind-closed-door meetings will be largely about "What staff member do you think reported this?" The outward focus may appear to be about cleaning up the wrongdoings, but the tacit goal will be to seek and eliminate the person who complained. It's a cynical point of view, but this is the reality I have experienced in multiple settings with different companies. That said, there are reasons to call corporate compliance, just as there are reasons not to.

In some instances, the Voltaire will also descend upon a facility on the heels of a critical incident – a death or suicide in the facility or some other serious incident that has gained traction with external investigators for instance. These corporate marauders will set-up temporary offices and workstations in the facility, all in an effort to go through documentation and scrub it for any liability, as well as to interview staff members. The staff interviews are done to find a person to whom they can assign blame and to seek out potential scapegoats if things get too bad. My advice for people dealing with this corporate team is to say as little as possible, and when you do speak to them, do your own documentation of the conversations. In fact, whenever possible, follow up with an email summarizing your conversation with them in an effort to document it. These people are not there to protect you. They are there to protect the company.

Having this corporate team of evildoers descend upon your facility is not a pleasant experience, especially when they are doing so on the heels of your corporate compliance complaint. They will engage you in some of the most insincere double-dealing that you have ever experienced. That said, they serve a purpose for you as well, which is to add more information to your packet of whistleblower information.

One of the main reasons that I activate corporate compliance is so that they are unable to deny knowledge of wrongdoing and to eliminate their plausible deniability. Even if they work to cover things up, the trail of information leading right up to corporate will be there if you document it correctly. Document meetings and follow-up meetings with emails reviewing what was discussed so you have that document as well. Additionally, if they change or alter any documents and you have different versions of the same document, this can impugn their credibility down the road when both versions are presented to external investigators and even the FBI.

Agency Three

One of my earliest experiences with corporate compliance came when my position at Agency Three had me reporting directly to the CEO. As discussed in the prior chapter, I was working within a relatively large healthcare system and in a facility that had gotten into a lot of trouble with the state in which it operated. The problems at the facility were quite egregious and well publicized in the media. I was brought in with a new CEO to fix the problems in this facility. As I mentioned, the CEO was one who truly wanted to improve the patient care and eradicate any problems, and we began doing just that. Though there were some people still steeped in the old way of doing things, the CEO and I broke through excuses and did our best to improve programming which meant the cleaning up multiple departments. This included terminations of employees who wanted to continue on the trajectory of our past.

On a sunny afternoon, someone from the corporate compliance department appeared at the agency. In her meeting with me, to review two complaints she received about our facility, she advised that the complaints were about both me and the CEO. More specifically, two individuals had called confidentially and reported that they did not believe we possessed the skill set to do the job and they wanted corporate to step in and hire people with more experience than they believed we had. As a leader, I like to be challenged, so I asked if there were any specific things mentioned in the complaint that I had done that had given that impression. I did express that I did not agree with the aspersion cast on either me or the CEO. In fact, I truly believed we were both competent enough to do our jobs well, but in the spirit of always improving I was curious about specifics.

In response, I was told that our corporate headquarters takes these complaints with a grain of salt and that they consider the source. I was also advised that for the first two years of new leadership, they mostly just disregard any complaints about that leadership. She went on to further explain that the two people who called in the confidential complaints were the Director of Human Resources and the Director of Nursing. It was long my belief that the Director of Human Resources was a barrier to our progress, and I had been pushing the CEO to terminate her. The Director of Nursing I actually liked and believed was doing a decent job, though, she was a little reactive at times.

Fortunately for both of these individuals, the CEO and I were not retaliatory individuals and we continued to do the best job that we could without terminating them. Both individuals remained employed at the facility, but with frequent undertones from corporate asking, "Do you think they need to be moved on yet?" By filing their corporate compliance complaint, in the eyes of our corporate headquarters, they had done more damage to their ability to remain than they did mine and the CEO's. After all, we had actually improved our reputation with the state. In improving our reputation, we also improved the number of referrals we received and, therefore, we improved the agency's financial stability.

———

In other facilities I worked at, I found myself being the author of corporate compliance letters and emails. I prefer letters and emails over calls because letters and emails are additional sources of documentation. I have submitted written corporate compliance complaints both with my signature on them and anonymously. This is a very personal decision. Some people are afraid to lose their jobs because it equates to a loss of income and a loss to their family's stability. Some people feel that they are not financially able to sustain that, or that it will cause too much stress on the family. When evaluating the decision to file a corporate compliance complaint or not, there are multiple points I'd like to make.

Foremost, we should always want to make the strongest possible case for the patients. The patients are the reason we are in our respective healthcare facilities. How can we justify not speaking up forcefully when wrongdoing occurs? If you endeavor to minimize a wrongdoing as not having a direct impact on a patient, I would suggest that turning away is actually a cascading transgression that promulgates more cascading transgressions. If a staff member is indifferent to rules, I'd suggest it is only a matter of time before that person causes serious harm to a patient. In many healthcare settings, turning a blind eye to a problem, even for just a few minutes, can cause irreparable harm to a patient. So, for these reasons, I suggest the question should not be *if* you should report, but *how*, anonymously or with your name attached.

If you do so anonymously, as I have stated, conversations about your complaint will become about who reported the given wrongdoing. The anonymous report often leads to more emphasis on catching the person who reported it instead of fixing the wrongdoing. Sadly, there is no denying that reporting or filing complaints with your name attached is often employment suicide at the agency you are complaining about. In some cases, however, they do remedy the problem. In such cases they may actually resent you for reaching out to corporate compliance and not going directly to the immediate supervisor whom everyone knows not to trust, but that corporate will not terminate. That said, if you report without your name on a complaint, you should realize that you may still be found out and terminated.

If you did not file a complaint with your name attached, you will have a difficult time proving that they knew it was you and that your termination was retaliatory. Putting your name to a complaint means they cannot deny the complaint was from you. Once there is no denying the complaint was from you, there will be an opportunity to watch out for retaliation and measure the temporal proximity of that retaliation. You can save all documents for your packet and add it all to a chronology of events.

For some people this is an untenable situation. One of the main reasons it is often untenable is because so few people have the courage to speak up in the first place. If more healthcare workers spoke up and reported things, it would not be so difficult for others to do it as well. Even better, if teams of people called collectively, they often have far more power as a group.

Chapter Five

Unfaithful Angels

This chapter is not about the colleagues who sat next to you and turned a blind eye to misconduct. Rather, this chapter is about the unfaithful angels who loom in our accrediting, licensing, and protective agencies who thematically fail to protect patients. It is about those whose job it is to investigate and protect but fall woefully short of their stated purpose. That said, this chapter is not intended to be ignominious toward these individuals or entities. This chapter is intended to be a cautionary tale that one should not, when blowing the whistle, look toward these entities with exhortation. They will not save you, and they often will not save the patients. Even though their fiduciary duties indicate they are obligated to protect, one cannot count on these unfaithful angels.

Indeed, these agencies often have competing interests that do not always align with the whistleblower. They often do not align with the patient either. They may be of some value, but they are also highly unlikely to align with you or do much about your concerns, even if patient lives are at risk. That is not to say they should not be a step in your whistleblower process. In fact, they should be. If you are specific enough when writing to these agencies, they will often validate your concerns with citations of the facility and demand the agency provide corrective action plans. This may appear futile because agencies are often cited for the same things over and over and submit the same aimless plans for improvement. This does, however, give you information, from a source other than yourself, that you can add to your packet for future use. Simply, you may find the unfaithful angels useless, but their paperwork can be immensely helpful later.

Let's continue our discussion about unfaithful angels with the dissolution that a national accreditation is somehow meaningful or indicative of high-quality patient care. It simply is not. There are countless examples of a nationally accredited programs in which patients have been abused and the agency has provided thematically substandard care.

Accrediting agencies such as The Joint Commission (TJC), formerly known as Joint Commission on Accreditation of Healthcare Organizations (JCAHO), is a nonprofit agency that accredits hospitals and healthcare facilities around the world. Agencies often pay tens of thousands of dollars for a site survey that will enable them to obtain the The Joint Commission gold seal of approval. The Joint Commission accredits approximately 80% of the hospitals in the U.S.A. (Lovern 2001). The agency touts itself by espousing, "We shape best practices and establish the most rigorous standards to raise the bar on performance" (The Joint Commission website). One of the hallmark tenets of The Joint Commission is their perceived role in Quality Care and Patient Safety. Topics on this hallmark tenet are espoused monthly through The Joint Commission's own *Journal on Quality and Patient Safety.*

The Joint Commissions funding is heavily dependent on healthcare organizations paying for their initial site survey and paying to maintain ongoing accreditation. While charging agencies to give them a gold seal of approval does not necessarily mean there is anything nefarious going on, there are examples that make you wonder how a healthcare entity received accreditation from The Joint Commission, and kept it, amid pervasive patterns of wrongdoing. There exist multiple examples of this, and it could be fodder for an entire book. I will punctuate some examples in this chapter.

The Wall Street Journal (Armour 2017) underscores my point by explaining The Joint Commission rarely withdraws its gold seal of approval from hospitals. The article quotes Dr. Ashish Jha, a health-policy researcher at Brown University, who explains the data "shows accreditation is basically meaningless—it doesn't mean a hospital is safe… It's clearly a failed system and time for a change." Moreover, the article aptly points out that members of The Joint Commission governing board are also in senior leadership at multiple hospitals accredited by The Joint Commission.

The healthcare accreditation industry is a multimillion-dollar business, with accolades like The Joint Commission's gold seal of approval offering no discernable or statistically significant difference in patient care or outcomes (Lam et. al. 2018). In fact, the

Joint Commission takes in annual revenue in excess of $120 million dollars (McKinney 2010), primarily from the fees it charges hospitals to be bestowed with its seal (Gaul 2005). Loss of accreditation means loss of revenue for The Joint Commission and there are ample examples of facilities receiving The Joint Commission gold seal of approval on the heels of significant substandard care.

Kids Peace

One salient example of The Joint Commission bestowing its gold seal of accreditation on a program with systemic issues is throughout the Kids Peace programs. Indeed, the problems that plague Kids Peace have been sustained over several years and appear to have little or no impact on their Joint Commission accreditation. Kids Peace operates a flagship hospital and treatment campus in Bethlehem, PA. Among the services they provide are an acute care hospital, residential treatment programs, and foster care programs. Kids Peace has programs that span across multiple states. These programs have enjoyed The Joint Commission Gold Seal of approval throughout their turbulent history.

In May of 1993, it was reported that a 12-year-old boy died at Kids Peace after a counselor sat on him during a physical hold (Cassler 1993). The media reports indicate that the boy who died was autistic and suffered from asthma. Later that year, in December 1993, a 14-year-old boy also died from asphyxiation during a physical restraint (Washburn 1999). The problems that permeated Kids Peace, however, have spanned the course of several years.

In 2007, *McClatchy - Tribune Business News* published a story on the thematic problems at Kids Peace. The article revealed, "Seven youths suffered broken bones while being restrained this year" (Assad 2007, p. 1). Indeed, the articles findings continue, "staff members were forcibly restraining out-of-control youths several times a day" (Assad 2007, p. 1). The article continues, "[between] July 2006 and July 2007, police made 159 trips to the main Kids Peace campus." (Assad 2007, p. 3). The problems were so bad that the state did step in and temporarily halted admissions to the program. They did not, however, shut Kids Peace down.

In April 2008, according to media reports, two 16-year-old girls, while being transported to a Narcotics Anonymous meeting, obtained methadone pills from a staff member who was driving them in her personal car (Assad 2008). According to the article, the two girls shared 28 methadone pills and both became unresponsive after returning to Kids Peace. Both girls were subsequently taken to the hospital. One of the girls died and the other is said to have suffered permanent nerve damage (Assad 2008). The article in *Morning Call* (Assad 2008) cites a report from the Pennsylvania Department of Public Welfare and reports that a state investigation into the death of a Kids Peace resident found the agency had not property supervised the residents and allowed the residents access to narcotics.

On November 3, 2018 the U.S. Department of Labor - Occupational Safety and Health Administration (OSHA) fined Kids Peace more than $14,000 for workplace violations.

According to the citation report, Kids Peace committed a serious violation of the OSHA Act of 1970 Section (5)(a)(1). The report adds, "The employer did not furnish employment and a place of employment which was free from recognized hazards that were causing or likely to cause death or serious physical harm to employees in that employees are exposed to the hazard of work place violence" (OSHA Report 2018, p. 1).

With such a long, tenuous history of abuse and neglect, you might wonder how Kids Peace could possibly still be licensed and how they could have remained accredited. This is particularly true since there are so many sources citing wrongdoing by Kids Peace staff. For example, you have coroners reports of kids being suffocated and injured in holds and you have OSHA reports citing how unsafe the environment of care is. Yet these multiple sources were not enough to give pause to The Joint Commission or state licensing officials. At least not pause enough to put an end to the abuse and shut the place down for the thematic violations and breaches of good faith and fair dealing with patients.

Unfortunately, Kids Peace is not the only example of accreditation being maintained, or awarded, in facilities with substantial wrongdoing. The lack of significant action that proliferates through an entire system of care has a profound impact on the lives of others.

Cases like that of Charles Cullen, a nurse who intentionally murdered more than 40 patients in hospitals over the course of 16 years (George 2004), are made possible because the people and the systems fail. The investigation into Nurse Cullen revealed several systemic failures spanning at least six facilities over 16 years, including multiple entities doing nothing about several performance issues of Mr. Cullen's and failing to report their concerns to his licensing board (Peterson 2003). All six facilities where Mr. Cullen murdered patients were, and remain, accredited by The Joint Commission and are licensed by their respective states.

There are reasons these unfaithful angels fail to protect patients, and there are two common excuses that I regularly hear. Perhaps you have heard them as well. The first, and perhaps most frustrating, is "Where will we send these patients if we close this place down?" The other is a concern about the ability of the agencies, particularly those with deep pockets, to fend off citations with protracted litigation. Although licensing agencies and accrediting agencies are two distinctly different entities, they both often fail to act strongly enough, and the consequences to patients are often life-altering.

Licensing entities are very reluctant to revoke licenses and close places down. In my experience, this is sometimes because of the belief that the patients will not have other places to go if their current agency is shut down. This is particularly true of institutions that serve the troubled-teen industry. Troubled teens are sometimes very hard to place, and these facilities often act as storage facilities for some of the most difficult-to-place children. That said, there is certainly not a lot of research showing that the troubled teen industry is effective in improving lives and, as you now know, there are a number of media accounts and citation reports illustrating they actually cause great harm.

For lack of better options, there is an incentive to keep places open. This is particularly true for large facilities with lots of patients who would need to be relocated and facilities with deep pockets that enable them to fight licensing entities to stay open. Anecdotally, smaller organizations without a lot of money seem to get shut down with more frequency than the big for-profit institutions. More research should be done in this area to test my anecdotal hypothesis.

Accrediting agencies also rely on facilities being open to collect their fees. In some cases, these fees are tens of thousands of dollars per facility. The accreditation process is expensive, but there are also multiple options. As mentioned, the Joint Commission is the most popular by far, accrediting some 80% of healthcare facilities (Lovern 2001). If The Joint Commission pulls an agency's accreditation, the agency can simply take its money elsewhere and try with a different accrediting agency. *The Wall Street Journal* revealed that from 2014–2016, hundreds of hospitals failed to meet The Centers for Medicare & Medicaid Services (CMS) requirements for violations they believed "caused or were likely to cause a risk of serious injury or death to patients," but the article found that less than 1% of these bad facilities had their accreditations revoked by The Joint Commission (Armour 2017). Simply, The Joint Commission is unlikely to revoke an agency's accreditation, even in the most egregious cases.

Moreover, I believe that when The Joint Commission surveys a facility of a company that owns hundreds of facilities across the country, the idea of giving one facility a failing report and potentially losing the business of hundreds of other facilities owned by the same corporation is quite daunting to them. Simply, there is a real fiscal disincentive for an accrediting agency to revoke or not accredit a healthcare facility within a corporation that owns multiple facilities. For this reason, they are probably far more likely to cite problems and request action plans to improve, rather than to revoke, an accreditation. As such, agencies are often cited repeatedly for the same types of violations.

Again, my purpose here is not to totally discredit licensing and accrediting agencies or even to cast them as dishonorable. I'm confident that they would project plenty of rhetoric to punctuate all the good that they believe they do. My intent here is to portray a realistic perspective of their role in your own whistleblowing. That is, don't delude yourself into thinking that these unfaithful angels will do anything more than provide you with documentation to substantiate, or maybe even discredit, your assertions about an organization's wrongdoings. I will illustrate how I have put them to use in Chapters 7 and 8.

It is also quite important to note here, there is a distinct difference between a state investigator and a disability-rights advocate. While both investigate complaints, they do come from separate worlds and are of similar purpose.

The state investigators are supposed to ensure agencies follow state standards. State investigators get a complaint, investigate the complaint, and close the complaint. Quite frankly, I don't find them particularly useful in terms of being strong advocates for patients. State investigators complete public reports after each complaint visit. Those become part of the public record and can become quite useful for whistleblower and other lawsuits against an agency. In fact, they often serve as a third-party validation of your concerns, so for this reason alone it is worth reporting things to them.

State licensing agencies are, however, governed with state bureaucracy. The bureaucracies generally do not like to keep cases open, and several states pressure workers to close investigations promptly. As noted before, they are also often afraid of agencies that are part of large health systems. One state investigator, frustrated by the lack of her state agency's tenacity against my employer, ended up quitting over it and going to work doing inventory at an amusement park. She claimed she was pressured to close cases without what she believed would be a thorough investigation. Another state investigator and I had a conversation about why they didn't seem to be doing much about the allegations of abuse or the repeated violations the agency continues to accrue. She replied, "You know they have deep pockets and they can sue us if we keep going in there, right?" She explained the state was afraid to keep citing agencies with very deep pockets because they were concerned about being sued for harassment by the facility. The sad reality is that licensing entities frequently disappoint whistleblowers and patients, while at the same time emboldening wrongdoers and abusers.

State licensing agencies and agencies responsible for placing children often leave children to perish in healthcare institutions in spite of past knowledge of wrongdoing. For example, *The*

Chicago Tribune ran a story in 2010 on the failures of the Illinois Department of Children and Families and the Illinois Department of Public Health on their persistent problem of failing to protect children in psychiatric hospitals from physical and sexual abuse. The *Tribune* article alleged that at least 18 new cases of rape or sexual abuse have been reported in area psychiatric hospitals since a story on the same issues broke two years prior (Jackson and Marx 2010).

Similarly, Chicago's Lakeshore Hospital has been plagued by years of abuse and fraud allegations. The abuse alleged at Lakeshore includes both physical and sexual abuse. Jackson (2011) reports that allegations were known to lawmakers spanning at least the time period of 2008–2011. Worse, a lawsuit filed on behalf of 7 children, who report they experienced sexual abuse and chemical restraints, alleges hospital staff and child welfare officials worked collectively to cover up the abuses (Eldeib 2019).

In his book about the traumatic abuse he both endured and witnessed, Allen Knoll describes a horrific incident in which a young boy in the program, where he resided as a child, was beaten unconscious by staff members. The boy had to be taken to a local hospital by ambulance because the abuse was so severe. The incident prompted an external investigation of the incident. Allen recalls his personal encounter with the unfaithful angels:

"The workers noticed me because I was so young
and they took me to their car and asked me how
everyone was treated. They had tape recorders and

notepads out. This made me nervous. At first, I
didn't want to say anything, but eventually I broke.
I told them everything! I told them I had personally been beaten and that other students had been
beaten much worse than me...To my horror, they
left me! I could not believe it. To this day, I have
no idea how this school could have possibly stayed
open after this." (Knoll 2018, p. 37)

After the unfaithful angels did nothing, Allen recalls the
impact this had on the staff:

"This incident seemed to encourage the staff
because things got much worse at the school...staff
had learned that they could get away with cruelty
and it didn't take long before they were back at it"
(Knoll 2018, p. 38).

For the reasons punctuated above, I often find disability rights advocates far more useful. For one, they are usually
called in to a case by a legal guardian to help advocate for, and
protect, a child or disabled adult. There are other ways they can
be activated, but they are generally invited in by a loved one to
help. Once they are invited into a case, they generally follow it.

These advocates usually do not face the same pressure to
close the case as state investigator's do. Meaning, they ensure
their clients are getting the best care possible by being involved
in multiple aspects of their treatment in an ongoing way. If

they see that the patient is not getting the best care, they will advocate for the removal of the patient from the program and find an alternative and better placement. They also can help patients gather information for lawsuits and can help find their clients lawyers to sue for relief if that is indicated. In Agency Two, for example, the disability rights advocate funneled multiple patients to lawyers, some of whom eventually filed lawsuits against the agency. The patient lawsuits alleged medical neglect, physical abuse, sexual abuse, and even wrongful death.

Additionally, disability-rights advocates also gather information and work collaboratively with state investigators and licensing regulators. They can often serve as an independent verifier of a whistleblower's information. There is often a notable difference when a disability rights advocate delivers information to the state and not the whistleblower, who can sometimes be cast aside as a disgruntled employee or a problematic individual.

Disability-rights advocates actually do not belong in a book chapter alongside unfaithful angels. They are often the only people who advocate for children and adults who desperately need support and assistance. I decided to include them here because they often work in concert with the unfaithful angels and can often serve to improve the effectiveness of state licensing boards and other agencies. They also use information that people provide them to advocate for policy changes that impact all healthcare organizations. Moreover, they are also commonly referred to as human rights advocates.

Chapter Six

On Those Who Came Before Us

Many people are familiar with whistleblowers by virtue of hearing about people who came before us. Some of the highest-profile and widely publicized cases serve to dot the whistleblower landscape with both cautionary tales and punctuate the risks associated with speaking up. There are even a few stories of people being rewarded with (what most would consider) large sums of money. Whistleblowers are important assets through every sector of our government and throughout our systems of care. Healthcare whistleblowing is no exception. Let us stand on the shoulders of those who came before us.

Government-employee whistleblower cases tend to be particularly high profile, but healthcare whistleblowers can become high profile as well. Throughout this chapter, I will highlight some of the most prominent whistleblower cases. This is not to dilute the value of lower-profile whistleblowers. There can be no doubt that whistleblowers, of all stripes, save lives.

Some high-profile government employee whistleblowers include:

- Brian Murphy, the former head of the intelligence branch at DHS, blew the whistle on the Trump administration, alleging that he was told to alter intelligence reports. Mr. Murphy alleged that he was advised by supervisors to minimize the level of threat that organizations including white supremacists create. (Kanno-Youngs & Goldman 2020).
- Lt. Col. Alexander Vindman blew the whistle on President Donald Trump for abusing his power by soliciting help from a foreign government to aid his election campaign. This information led to subsequent investigations and eventually Trump's impeachment trial. Trump was impeached by Congress and acquitted by the Senate. Two days after the acquittal, Trump fired witness Gordon Sondland and Alexander Vindman. His brother Lt. Col. Yevgeny Vindman was also asked to step down (Fandos 2020).
- Edward Snowden blew the whistle in 2013 by releasing information on PRISM, a government surveillance program conducted by NASA. Some deemed Snowden a hero and whistleblower; others considered him a traitor (Parker 2014). Snowden was criminally charged under the Espionage Act for the release of government documents to

the public, at the same time, he is credited with opening a national dialogue about the "balance between privacy and civil liberties" (*The Washington Post* 2013).

- William Sanjour spent thirty years in the Environmental Protection Agency (EPA) blowing the whistle on multiple incidents until his retirement in 2001. During his tenure he faced retaliation, work reassignments, work demotions, and multiple fights, one of which led to landmark government whistleblower protection legislation in 1995 (Carozza 2007).

- W. Mark Felt Sr. is perhaps one of the most notorious government whistleblowers. Known at the time only as "Deep Throat," Felt worked in the Federal Bureau of Investigations (FBI) and leaked information about the Nixon campaign's involvement in the Watergate scandal, which eventually led to the resignation of President Richard Nixon. Felt remained an anonymous whistleblower from 1974–2005, at times declaring, "It was not I, and it was not I" when asked if he was Deep Throat (Marcus 2005, p. 1).

As mentioned in prior chapters, almost all whistleblowers report some sort of adverse consequences to their actions. The "what became of them" could probably serve as fodder for an entire book. But, there is little doubt that whistleblowers, in spite of adverse actions they may receive, truly make a positive difference. While there are obvious similarities among all whistleblowers, I believe that healthcare whistleblowers have a unique quandary before them because of the direct, and sometimes immediate, impact on patient lives.

Healthcare whistleblowers are also often navigating between both the private and public sectors. This does not just speak to the whistleblower's employer, but also to the entities the whistleblower must work with during his efforts. If we are to activate all viable systems in our efforts, we will be blowing the whistle to, and about, both private and public organizations. This can bring forth a unique set of challenges as the protections, and the viable options we can take, vary considerably in each arena.

For example, healthcare workers who works in a private-sector hospital will likely be activating public-sector advocates such as licensing agencies, protective agencies, and the like. They may also activate private-sector human rights advocates and lawyers. When done well, successfully activating all the entities available to the healthcare whistleblower, can serve to make the whistleblowers' cases ineradicable.

The laws that surround whistleblower protection are incredibly complicated and vary considerably by jurisdiction. For this reason, it is always best to bring as much documentation as you can, about as much wrongdoing as you can, to your employment lawyer to determine the best course of action for your case.

Whistleblowing in healthcare is particularly important because of both morality and the direct impact failing to care has on patients. In addition to the impact substandard care has on a patient's life, healthcare whistleblowers are an important moral line of defense against fraud being perpetrated against the federal government. The federal government often recognizes the importance of healthcare whistleblowers through Qui Tam cases. Qui Tam cases are rare, but have become increasingly more popular and frequent. The federal government recognizes the importance of these cases and, as such, rewards whistleblowers who bring them forward with a share of the financial amount recovered. Additionally, if the federal government decides to pursue a whistleblower's Qui Tam case, the burden and expense of prosecuting the case will be shared with the Federal Government.

Since the wrongful termination for whistleblowing laws often vary by state, whistleblowers who have good evidence of fraud often find the Qui Tam fraud cases are far more lucrative and easier to pursue. Qui Tam is a Latin phrase indicating "he who sues on behalf of the king" and himself. In a Qui Tam case, private individuals, referred to as realtors, bring forth a case of fraud perpetrated against the government, in which the government can recover money (Ruhnka et. al. 2000, Ceasar 2006). If the case is picked up by the federal government and money is recovered, a percentage of the recovered amount is paid to the whistleblower who brings forth the case. The recovery for the whistleblower varies and can be up to 30%, with an average of 18%, of the amount recovered by the federal government (Webb 2000, Rosenberg 1998). Additionally, the whistleblower (or realtor) bringing the case must have direct knowledge of the fraud and the fraud must not already be in the public domain (Rosenberg 1998).

The whistleblower percentage of the recovery depends somewhat on the roadmap that the individual delivers to the federal government. Simply put, the more documented proof you have, the better. Additionally, providing them with witness lists of people they can also interview, people who can provide salient details, also helps. These cases take a long time to adjudicate and can become very complicated, so you really need to talk to a Qui Tam lawyer about pursing this type of case. Qui Tam cases are also complicated by the fact that few lawyers know how to properly write and file them. Similarly, the lawyers who do know how to file them require a lot of evidence and hard-copy proof of the claims made, so the packet of information you bring to a Qui Tam lawyer has to be very solid.

That said, once a Qui Tam case does close, it is often very lucrative for the whistleblower. According to the United States Department of Justice, in spite of the global pandemic and courts being closed for portions of 2020, the federal government recovered $1.6 billion in Qui Tam settlements in 2020, $309 million of that going to individuals who exposed the fraud. Qui Tam filings have been on the rise for years and 2020 was no different. In 2020, Qui Tam cases were filed at an average of 13 per week, 80% of them coming from the healthcare industry

(United States Department of Justice, Justice News, January 14, 2021).

There are some truly notable Qui Tam settlements and I will highlight some of the biggest cases below, but I must reiterate that these cases remain pretty rare. It is my belief they should not be, and with cases on the rise and fraud so rampant, the cases broached here will likely be eclipsed by newer and bigger cases.

The Case of Quorum Health Group/Columbia/HCA Inc.

In 2000, Quorum Health Group/HCA Inc. (formerly known as Columbia HCA) paid well over $1 billion in penalties to the Department of Justice. HCA Inc. was once the largest for-profit hospital chain in the U.S. They are also credited with participation in one of the largest healthcare fraud schemes in U.S. history. Multiple whistleblowers provided the Department of Justice with information to help the FBI investigate this case. According to the June 26, 2003 press release by the Department of Justice, the government recovered $1.7 billion from HCA Inc. $631 million of this settlement were civil penalties and damages arising from false claims filed by HCA Inc. At the time, this investigation represented the most comprehensive healthcare fraud investigation ever undertaken by the federal government. It remains one of the most notorious and biggest healthcare fraud cases to date.

Robert D. McCallum, Jr., Assistant Attorney General for the Civil Division, said, "This settlement brings to a close the largest multi-agency investigation of a healthcare provider that the United States government has ever undertaken and demonstrates the Department of Justice's ongoing resolve and commitment to pursue all types of fraud on American taxpayers and healthcare program beneficiaries." It is easily argued that this case would not have been so successful without the help of whistleblowers, who in this case were rewarded with a settlement in excess of $151 million.

Part of the case against HCA Inc. began in 1990 with James Alderson, a Chief Financial Officer (CFO) at North Valley, who broached issues of irregular accounting with the company. An article written by Grover Porter (2003) about the incident provides great detail about Alderson's story. According to the article, "Alderson was told that Quorum (a division of HCA Inc.) created a secret set of books. The second set of books would be used as a basis for reporting higher-than-actual expenses to the government for reimbursement." The article further adds, "He refused to use the secret accounting method devised by HCA, however, saying that it was illegal and unethical." The article notes that James Alderson was terminated approximately five days later. In another article, Alderson reported, "They said things weren't working out and it looked like I wasn't going to be a team player" (Taylor 1999, p. 3).

Indeed, James Alderson was fired in close temporal proximity (within five days) of reporting fraud or abuse. Moreover, he met another basic canon of a whistleblower case – his refusal to participate in the fraud (although there are some instances in which you may still report fraud and receive a recovery, even if you had previously participated in the fraud).

Among the major reasons Alderson's case was effective was the fact that he secured documentation of the fraud perpetrated against the federal government. With this proof, he was able to file a Qui Tam suit in 1993. That said, the Porter (2003) article broaches how his family struggled for several years after Alderson was terminated in 1990. According to the article, "The family moved to five different towns as Alderson tried to balance earning a paycheck with gathering evidence." His wife reported feeling as if she were in the witness protection program without the witness protection program's benefit of income and protection.

Five years after Alderson was terminated, he was joined in the whistleblowing effort against Columbia/HCA Inc. by John Schilling, although Alderson did not immediately know it. Schilling, an employee of Columbia/HCA, also became aware of fraud being perpetrated by the hospital corporation against the federal government. According to David Hilzenrath in an article in *The Washington Post* (1998), Schilling resigned from the company in 1995. Shortly after leaving, he filed a Qui Tam lawsuit and reported the fraud to the FBI. He later returned to work for Columbia/HCA Inc. and served as an informant for the FBI in an effort to gather more information about the fraud throughout the company. Even after the FBI raid, John continued his investigation and continued to report what he learned to the FBI. In December 1998 he was outed as an informant by the FBI/DOJ as their case came to a head (Hilzernath 1998).

There are many other Qui Tam cases where the whistleblowers receive substantial sums of money. Some others include:

- Rev. John Corapi and Joseph F. Zerga blew the whistle on a Redding (CA) hospital and will share a Qui Tam settlement of $8.1 million (15% of the total recovery), according to the settlement agreement (Walsh 2004).
- Elin Baklid-Kunz blew the whistle on Halifax Hospital Medical Center (FL), providing the federal government documentation of "more than a decade of billing fraud, unnecessary hospital admissions, inappropriate spinal surgeries and illegal kickbacks to doctors" (Jameson 2013, p. 1). Baklid-Kunz's portion of the Qui Tam settlement was $20.8 million. In an article about her experience, she expresses sadness about being shunned and reports that throughout the experience she learned who her true friends were (Swisher 2014).
- Kalispell Regional Healthcare (MT) reached a settlement agreement of $24 million with the federal government over allegations of healthcare fraud brought by an employee, Jon Mohatt (Gardner 2019).
- Doctors Choice Home Healthcare Inc. agreed to pay $5.8 million to settle Qui Tam allegations

brought by former employees Corina Herbold,
Sara Billings, Misty Sykes, and Marina Es-
choyez-Quiroga (Justice Department 2020). The
allegations included violations of the Anti-Kick-
back Statute (providing compensation for referrals),
The Stark Law (providing bonuses for referrals),
and upcoding billing to Medicare for unnecessary
services (Justice Department 2020).

Qui Tam whistleblower cases are easy to find online. Experts
believe that the Department of Justice widely publicizes these
cases in an effort to prompt more Qui Tam whistleblowers to
come forward. Indeed, the large settlement amounts are truly
eye-catching. That said, since these cases are actually quite rare
and take years for the government to prosecute, whistleblowers
are more likely to sue for things such as wrongful termination or
a similar law that captures how they were wrongfully terminated – for example, fired for being a member of a protected class.

Again, the more information you bring to an employment lawyer, the better. The employment lawyer will review
your packet of documentation and help decide which type of
case you might file, if any. If you have evidence of billing fraud
against the federal government programs (Medicaid, Medicare,
Tricare, etc.) you will want to speak to a lawyer who specializes
in Qui Tam cases.

Wrongful-termination case-settlement amounts are
difficult to find, so it is hard to illustrate how much money can
be recovered for the whistleblower in these cases. The inability

to capture this information fully is a result of several variables. For example, cases often begin with a large ask and then settle for much less. The ask is filed and becomes public record and, therefore, is sometimes publicized. These settlements, however, are often wrapped up in settlement agreements that prevent further discussion of the settlement amount.

Another reason settlement amounts are hard to write about is because the laws vary considerably by state. For example, one state may allow compensatory damages for the pain and suffering caused by being terminated for whistleblowing, while other states do not allow this to be included. Lastly, on the off chance your case goes to trial and the jury awards you financial compensation, larger verdicts are often appealed, set aside, or the amount changed by the judge. For the reasons outlined above, it becomes very difficult to ascertain settlement amounts in other types of wrongful termination cases.

That said, there are publicized cases in which the initial financial ask and the final settlement amounts are publicized. I will take a moment to illustrate just a few.

- Apria Healthcare Group Inc. (CA) was sued for wrongful termination by Victor M.G. Chaltiel for an initial ask of $7 million (Granelli 1995). Chaltiel was an executive at Apria Healthcare Group Inc. The final settlement was wrapped up in a settlement agreement and neither side has revealed the settlement amount (Granelli 1995).
- CooperRiis (NC) was sued for wrongful

termination by Laura Haas, a mental health therapist, after she was wrongfully terminated for reporting the illegal administration of medicine to patients. The case settled for $4 million (for both wrongful termination and punitive damages) in 2017 (Hamacher 2017).

- McGuire Memorial (PA) was sued by Brandy L. Roman, a nurse, who alleged she was wrongfully terminated for refusing to work overtime and after alerting her bosses that forcing overtime was a violation of law in Pennsylvania (Chikomo 2015). The judge in this case awarded Roman $121,869.93 and reinstated her position at McGuire (Baker 2017).

Moreover, in the spirit of punctuating cascading transgressions, McGuire Memorial was sued on behalf of four former clients in cases filed in 2019. The suits allege abuse, neglect, and two wrongful deaths (Mayo 2019). According to media reports, the incidents took place between 2017–2018. Two of the abusers who worked for the hospital were charged with nearly thirty criminal counts that include assaulting, endangering, and neglecting children in their care. The incidents included sexually explicit filming of minor residents as well (Suttles 2020).

The point I am trying to underscore in this chapter is that mechanisms exist for whistleblowers if they know how to effectively activate the systems that serve to protect them or provide them relief. Meanwhile, the healthcare workers are the only people who can protect patients from harm while in healthcare facilities. It is my sincere hope that this chapter, coupled with the others, serve to elucidate this point.

Chapter Seven

In Your Defense

I have frequently told colleagues that no one knows better than you do, meaning, healthcare laws are sometimes so nuanced that even lawyers struggle with some of the more subtle details that govern the healthcare field. In presenting and defending your case, be prepared to explain these nuanced and subtle gradations.

For example, after consulting with a lawyer on a wrongful death case, he explained to me that a healthcare agency was trying to claim that the client willed his own death. Simply, they were making an effort to portray that the client did not want to live any longer, rather than the more likely scenario of their own negligence of failing to properly care for and supervise him. Knowing the specific healthcare law that applied to this situation, I explained that the facility was either negligent for not sending a suicidal patient to a qualified hospital for a screening, to possibly be committed to an acute unit, or they were negligent for not supervising him. Since the facility was not licensed for acutely suicidal patients, they were, in fact, negligent either way. I was able to provide this lawyer with the exact law that was violated so that he could bring some minor relief to the patient's grieving family.

Kohn (2017) details how whistleblowers are more adept than regulatory agencies at detecting fraud. I believe the same is true of the whistleblower's ability to chronicle and effectively report other abuses as well. This includes medical errors, physical abuse, sexual abuse, and other maleficence. The ways in which healthcare workers can expose these wrongful actions are multifarious.

As you go about your work, read every email you receive once for the content and what you are supposed to do and then read it again for potential use in a future lawsuit. Once you have examined an email with this lens, print it and keep it. Emails are wonderful bodies of evidence. They also automatically time and date-stamp everything and come in quite handy when creating a timeline of events. As we have punctuated in prior chapters, in whistleblowing, the timeline of events is particularly salient. For this reason, emails can become important. Print that email you were sent months ago about the great job you are doing. Keep that email you were sent thanking you for a task well done. Keep the email about that agency policy not being followed. Keep the email about an incident of cascading transgression. People tend to put a wealth of information in emails which can become part of your body of evidence.

For the whistleblower, the fall from being a competent professional to a lone individual who is viewed by others with derision can happen quite quickly. You can be doing a great job for ten years and then the next day a new director is hired and the entire tone of an agency changes. With the stroke of a leadership change you might find yourself having worked in a great environment that abruptly degenerates into one of deception, fear, and unease.

Good performance evaluations, complimentary emails, and positive notes, do not just serve as evidence of better times. These pieces of documentation help to illustrate you are not as incompetent as they might make you out to be when you start speaking up. They are not just your own thoughts and feelings; they can become evidence and part of your whistleblower packet. These pieces of evidence can come to your defense and serve to illustrate the exact moment things changed for you in an organization.

Agency Four

My direct supervisor in Agency Four was an unassuming man who had no spine and did the bidding of his superiors and colleagues, even if these colleagues were in a lateral position, he backed down from them all the time. In addition, he frequently told us do to one thing and when others would criticize it, he would question why we did it to begin with. He never took responsibility for giving the order in the first place. It took me a while to figure out that this was how he operated. When I finally did, my colleagues were supportive. They told me that they did not warn me because I needed to find out for myself. Indeed, this boss was a profane figurehead with mock morals and ethics – a shame, really, because he did know his job well but did not possess the skill set to insist on things being done correctly.

My timeline of events in Agency Four abruptly changed when I started to complain about staffing on our units, frequent incidents, and concerns about the safety of our residents. In fact, it was within close temporal proximity to my effort to address these problems with senior leadership that the tone toward me abruptly changed. I had received positive performance evaluations and notes of jobs well done, but that all changed as soon as I spoke up.

Shortly after I spoke up about the agency's wrongdoings, my supervisor came into my office with a written document that was characterized as a verbal warning. We had never had any disciplinary conversations and considering the history of documentation I had about my previous performance, this took me quite by surprise. I calmly took a deep breath and began to read.

As I read, I saw that most of what was included was simply untrue. There were dates that were not correct and information that had been misconstrued, taken out of context, or was blatantly false. Inside, I was livid. On the outside, I appeared confident, mildly amused, and quite calm. I think all I said while reading was "hmm" once or twice and just continued to remind myself to remain calm. Positive self-talk and good breathing got me through this interaction. I was so dedicated to this job and improving the lives of my patients that I was floored this appeared to no longer matter.

My supervisor attempted to downplay the document, as if I could not see my termination coming. He made false and assuring comments like, "This is just a verbal warning" even though the document said otherwise. He uttered a few other statements like "We will help you improve over the next 90 days" and similar false platitudes that I know were just him trying to break the uncomfortable silence. He further advised, "You have to sign it and your signature means only that you saw it." I was also told that failure to sign it would be seen as insubordination and could result in immediate termination. As most disciplinary forms have, there was a space for comments. If I can offer no other advice, it would be to write the words "addendum to follow" and then sign it and calmly hand it back. If your disciplinary action form does not have space, write in the words "addendum to follow" anyway. Put it right over your signature if you have to, just make sure it is there and they know there is more to come.

After you write "addendum to follow" and sign the document, always ask for a copy. If you have any reservations that you may not be provided a copy, walk that form (in your own hand) and your boss to a copier and make a copy yourself. The most salient thing here is the inclusion of "addendum to follow." Say as little in the moment as possible. If you are asked if you have comments, questions, concerns, simply say you are going to take the time think about it. I also do my best to avoid timeframes. For example, "addendum to follow" means you will have my addendum when I'm done. Unless there is a company policy that an appeal or response must be filed in a day or two, then you probably have time. There is no hard and fast rule here, and this is not legal advice, but you don't want to let them pressure you and you don't want to provide an emotional response. Indeed, you want to provide them with a factual response. You need to know your company policy about appeals, chain of command, and how long you have to reply to things like disciplinary actions.

I quickly learned that "addendum to follow" can become one of the most powerful phrases at your disposal. It often puts people in fear of what you will write up in an addendum. Bad bosses do not want to be exposed with an explosive addendum that reveals their own wrongdoing to everyone who reads it. It can serve to keep supervisors on edge and takes back your power. It also gives you the time to discuss it and broach your reply with colleagues and even a lawyer if you choose to. Drafting a reply and having a lawyer review it can be very helpful.

In this particular "addendum to follow" scenario, in Agency Four, my supervisor appeared at my door less than an hour later explaining he was rescinding the writeup and he rescinded it in writing. My guess is that he did not want to see the addendum. I was not deluded enough to think that I was back in favor. I knew it was only a matter of time before they found a better and cleaner way to get rid of me.

From that point on, I began to gather even more evidence and paperwork to support my concerns about the programming, safety of residents, and safety of staff. It was not my intention to put a packet together for a lawsuit, but I did intend to put a packet together to force change within the program, even if in my absence.

It was my steadfast belief that Agency Four had a senior

leadership team that needed to be removed for the best interests of the patients. Unlike many mental health organizations, this particular agency was very well funded and had the resources to put together a decent treatment program. I knew the barriers to this were the senior leadership team. Ironically, I did not think my direct supervisor was the actual root of the problem. As noted above, this man just did what he was told; and if told to do the right thing, he probably would. He just appeared to lack the capacity and skill set to effectively advocate for anything in a meaningful way. We don't know what happens behind closed doors. Perhaps he did so behind closed doors, but he rarely supported his team against the leadership team that was frequently hostile toward his department.

———

The only difference, in my experience, among residential treatment programs in the teen industry is that some programs try to clean up the abuse and other programs try to cover up the abuse. Some, like Agency Four, have leadership teams that act indifferent to it. On one hand they did report all allegations of abuse, but on the other hand they did little to rectify a systemic and recurring problem. Staff logs, emails, incident reports, treatment plans, internal memos, etc. all served to illustrate the lack of improvement and the lack of safety in this agency. Agency Four was a small nonprofit; these thematic problems can often be compounded in large and complex health systems.

Large and complex health systems are quite expert at

minimizing risk to the company and are often quick to claim that the incidents at one facility are not indicative of wrongdoing in other facilities. As healthcare employees in large systems of care, we badly want this belief to be palpable. If this belief is palpable, we can rationalize our staying within a bad system by claiming the wrongdoing and malfeasance systemic throughout the company somehow does not permeate into our facility. Unfortunately, the actual data simply does not support this assertion.

The data supports that, in environments of cascading transgressions, the cascade dampens and drips through the entire corporation and eventually affects many facilities. In healthcare we often talk about corporate culture. If a parent company's corporate culture is such that a facility can commit fraud and provide substandard patient care, that is often the culture of the parent company. If a parent company applies pressure on individual facilities for more profit to excel overall growth of the company, that often leads to substandard care and patient harm. There are multiple companies where this narrative bodes true.

HCA Inc.

The fraud case involving HCA Inc. that is broached in this book began with wrongdoing being exposed at one hospital. Over the course of the investigation, investigators found that similar transgressions had cascaded to impact more than 100 of HCA's facilities. In fact, according to a Department of Justice press release (June 26, 2003), at the conclusion of the case, multiple transgressions occurred across the company that included:

- Multiple lawsuits alleging that HCA engaged in a series of schemes to defraud Medicare, Medicaid and TRICARE
- Eight counts, from multiple facilities, of making false statements to the United States.
- Multiple lawsuits settled alleging that HCA hospitals and home health agencies unlawfully billed Medicare, Medicaid and TRICARE for claims generated by the payment of kickbacks and other illegal remuneration to physicians in exchange for referral of patients.
- Columbia Management Companies, Inc., pled guilty to one count of conspiracy to pay kickbacks and other monetary benefits to doctors in violation of the Medicare Antikickback Statute.
- Allegations and a settlement that certain company-owned hospitals billed Medicare for unallowable costs incurred by a contractor that operated HCA wound care centers, and for a non-covered drug that the contractor manufactured and sold to hospital patients.
- Guilty plea concerning cost report fraud included a charge related to wound care center costs. HCA's wound care center management contractor.
- Allegations concerning the transfer of patients

from HCA facilities to other facilities and the claiming of excessive costs for those transfers.

- Allegations and settlement that a hospital in the system submitted false claims in Medicare cost reports by inflating its entitlement to funds to treat indigent patients and by shifting employee salary costs in order to increase its reimbursement from the federal healthcare program.
- Settled allegations made by Michael Marine that HCA improperly shifted its home office costs to hospitals.

It would be naïve to think that the aforementioned fiscal issues did not contribute to a culture in which substandard care would proliferate in HCA facilities and remain until this day. After all, transgressions do cascade. By way of illustration, in more recent hospital reports the following has been noted at multiple HCA Inc. facilities.

North Suburban Medical Center (Colorado) – In a June 11, 2020 inspection reports, cite the facility as being accountable for multiple violations. This includes an incident leading to a patient death. The areas of substandard care that North Suburban Medical Center was cited for include violations in the areas of:

Patient rights
Patient rights – care in a safe setting
QAPI – Quality and Performance Improvement

Patient Safety
Nursing Services
Staffing and Delivery of Care
Infection Control

Moreover, criminal fraud cases involving HCA Inc. facilities and subsidiaries continue to proliferate through the court systems around the country.

Similarly, large psychiatric systems of care are plagued with the same thematic issues. Psychiatric hospitals and treatment facilities frequently treat some of the most vulnerable individuals. People who are struggling with addiction, depression, anxiety, sexual abuse and other trauma. I have worked within these larger systems of care and am profoundly aware of the thematic issues that plague these corporations. The idea that maltreatment, fraud, and substandard care are limited to medical hospitals is simply untenable.

No facility or program is without incident. There is some truth to the claim by corporate leaders that they are simply unable to control all staff members all the time and that one or two bad ones do not mean an entire system is flawed. That said, when a large hospital chain has thematic and recurring problem, it likely means that these problems are steeped in their culture. Worse, many of these systems of care have become quite adept at covering up systemic issues of abuse and fraud. They achieve this by hiring profane figureheads with mock morals. They count on these individuals to support the corporations drive for profit and growth with slavish fealty. There are several ways that I have witnessed this being achieved. Foremost, it requires the tacit approval and cooperation of the unfaithful angels.

There is no doubt that whistleblowers have, and do, provide an invaluable role of improving our healthcare institutions. Indeed, "The act of reporting wrongdoing at work has shown to be an effective way to improve services, products and procedures. The hope is therefore that the stigma attached to the act gradually can change" (Bjorkelo & Macko 2012, p.74). Miceli & Near further explain, "Managers, employees and members of society need to undergo a cultural transformation such that whistleblowing is viewed as potentially positive for those involved. Only with this changed view of whistleblowing will it prove more effective as a mechanism for corporate and societal change" (Miceli & Near, 2005, p. 98).

The whistleblower process is filled with building blocks. Doing everything you can to foster change while working within the agency is often a first step. Gathering as much information as you can to corroborate your assertions is paramount to your success as a whistleblower. External entities are likely to care even less about your thoughts and feelings than your employer does.

As we discussed in chapter five, the unfaithful angels in external agencies can serve an invaluable role here. Accreditation reports, site surveys, human rights complaints, police calls, etc. can all serve to provide corroborating evidence of your assertions and are an excellent addition to your whistleblowing packet. These bodies of evidence can often be acquired with public records requests. In some states, these bodies of evidence are available online; in others they must be formally requested from each entity. Take the time to request them and put them into your packet of documentation and insert them into your timeline of events.

Similarly, filing detailed complaints with detailed information you know about wrongdoing can prompt one of the aforementioned reports. By way of illustration, if you know your agency has failed to call in an allegation of abuse to the state abuse hotline, you can report that to both the state hotline and the state licensing agency.

When filing any agency complaint with a state licensing board or other agencies, you need to be as specific as possible. Remember, these are often unfaithful angels and your allegation can be promptly dismissed if it is not detailed enough. In many cases, an investigator will show up at an agency and the full scope of their visit will be just on the limited, or not so limited, information provided in the complaint. As always, provide dates, times, staff involved, staff responses, where their documentation is actually kept (and hidden), etc. For example, in one facility where I worked, one binder by nursing had all the incident reports. If people did not show up and look at that specific binder, they would have no idea about agency incidents because they were not documented anywhere else.

Agency One

My detailed correspondence about Agency One serves to illustrate this point. In this communication. I'd like to highlight an ongoing and systemic problem with patient elopement for an acute care psychiatric unit – indeed, a very unsafe situation for patients, staff, and the community.

I detail the problem as follows:

> The elopement problem at [Agency One] is both a chronic and dangerous one. Patients were able to escape the supervision of the locked acute units on [date one], [date two], [date three], [date four], [date five], and [date six]. In [month of incident seven] another patient, the seventh patient since [date one], ran away with a key to an [Agency One] van in his pocket. This patient, like several others before him, was able to jump over the fence and elope from the inpatient acute care hospital. In [month of incident eight], another patient eloped the locked unit and had to be brought back by staff. This escape from the locked acute care inpatient facility marks what represents at least eight (8) elopements since [date one]. This is in violation of standard [xxx.xx(x)(x)] relating to PATIENT RIGHTS: CARE IN SAFE SETTING.

> Since [date eight], there have been additional elopements from the acute care secured locked units at [Agency One]. Most recently, on [date nine] a patient eloped from Unit (x) and was chased after by staff member [name]. Staff

member [name] caught the patient at an off-site location, [name of store] and returned him to the facility. Staff members are not permitted to chase after patients."

I was able to find state licensing board people to write to by finding their email addresses online. In addition, I copied the email to the governor's office, an email address also found online, in an effort to ensure there was meaningful followup. Sometimes you have salient individuals' email addresses through the regular course of business at work. You should keep these email addresses in your packet for future use.

When you include great detail in a complaint, it becomes hard to ignore. When the state investigators showed up at the agency, on this complaint, they were armed with specific dates, times, locations, and had an idea of what statute this all violated.

I was able to replicate this process at least six times over the course of a few months. In each instance, the state investigators were able to validate my complaint and generated a site survey report for each visit. I was then able to obtain all site surveys for Agency One through formal records requests. These site surveys serve as documentation in my whistleblower packet. This information can be combined with other information in the packet for use in a potential lawsuit or for handoff to the news media.

The media, however, is often considered an avenue of last resort. Moreover, taking the aforementioned steps first can serve as building blocks to foster the best media narrative.

Activating the Media

The media can become an invaluable and very effective part of helping blow the whistle on an organization's wrongdoing. In fact, we would not know about most of the abuse that occurs in healthcare facilities if not for the media. For this reason, I highly recommend putting together a comprehensive, local and national, media list. You can search and collect journalist information online. When compiling my own media list, I often search for journalists who have already written stories in the area of healthcare fraud and abuse. Journalists who seek to expose problems in healthcare are particularly valuable contacts to have on your media list. In many cases you can find journalists who have already written about large and complex health systems by searching online or in the bibliography of this book. It is also important to have both local and national media contacts on your list. One of the most salient reasons for a good media list is the near unlimited reach of the media and that media news stories often remain online forever. Indeed, a good news story can become an indelible part of an organization's narrative.

Nationally recognized media outlets seem particularly search-engine friendly, meaning that when an organization is searched online, the news story can appear on the first page of the search results to help inform and warn potential consumers. Additionally, don't be afraid to ask journalists to include things like the agency's parent company, the accrediting body (i.e., The Joint Commission), and the state entity responsible for licensing the facility in their stories. Including these other entities will help with search results and tie the entities to the wrongdoing at the facility that is the subject of the story. It may also put pressure on the named entities to do something about the problems in the facility.

Local media outlets are also valuable and should not be discounted when making your list. Local media will drill down on local politics and the agency's role in the community. If the agency presents a danger to residents in a community, such as frequent elopements from a secure facility or an unmitigated risk to public health, local media outlets will want to spotlight things like this in their coverage.

To be an effective whistleblower externally, you have to be adept at controlling the narrative. Any decent media outlet will reach out to your agency for comment. In almost all cases the comment will include phrases like "We deny the allegations" or "We have provided great care to many patients" or, worse, they will discount you as disgruntled or ineffective in the duties of your job. If you provide enough detail for the story, their comment will get lost in the broader narrative. If you can help illustrate that you have emails complimenting your work, but were retaliated against as soon as you spoke up, that stifles their narrative as well. Additionally, when the article is filled with site survey results, police call-log notes, and incident investigation results, people will remember the corroboration of the agency's wrongdoing above all else.

Similarly, large national media outlets want to break stories. If you already provided a big story to a local media outlet, the national outlet is unlikely to cover it unless you have something new to add that they deem significant. You can provide them new aspects to the story to keep them interested.

Again, don't be afraid to ask journalists to include specific information in a story. For example, the inclusion of the name of a parent company in a media story is important for multiple reasons. One, large healthcare corporations go to great lengths to distance themselves from the wrongdoing at a particular facility or hospital. The inclusion of the name of a parent company in the news story helps identify what parent company the facility belongs to. It also helps tie the parent company to the wrongdoing of the facility. Additionally, it helps identify thematic patterns throughout a company. If you can find a bunch of news stories about hospitals being short-staffed, neglecting patients, and they are all grouped to the same parent company, it would not be difficult to identify this as a broader management problem.

Agency Three

Agency Three was part of a large and complex health system that cared for vulnerable children. The agency had a history of frequent police calls and allegations of child abuse. As many healthcare professionals know, risk managers and senior leadership team members, sometimes try very hard to keep major incidents from proliferating into the public domain. Large health systems can generally overcome negative media attention, but none of them like it.

In some states, when an allegation of child abuse is reported, the state investigator is accompanied by the police, which triggers a police call in the police call log. At this particular agency, the CEO told me that we did not like to report all allegations of abuse because it triggers a police call, is entered into a police call log, and becomes public record. Worse, this CEO was willing to suggest that not all allegations of abuse in the state in which the agency operated were reportable, suggesting that we need to investigate first to assess the validity of the claim. When I respectfully pushed back, I was provided a printout taken from the state website that indicated "all reasonable allegations of abuse are reportable." Most healthcare professionals know that we are mandated reporters of abuse. Most of us are not child abuse investigators, as that title is usually reserved for state investigators. In my pushback, I explained that "reasonable allegations" meant that when a child came to school with a bruise, the teacher could not assume the bruise came from the child's parent. I added, when a patient makes a direct allegation of abuse against an agency staff member, the social worker is legally obligated to call it in to the state abuse hotline. This did not go over well with this CEO or the Trifecta of Abuse governing the agency.

I was actually surprised that my desire to follow my fiduciary responsibility of calling in (to the state abuse hotline) all allegations of abuse made by our patients was somehow problematic for this CEO. Indeed, in situation after situation and allegation after allegation, I was summoned to meetings with our CEO and my direct supervisor. In each meeting the CEO would try to dissuade us from calling allegations of abuse into the hotline. Worse, during this CEO's tenure, multiple patient deaths occurred.

During my tenure, there was a progressive escalation of attacks on my work and increased intimidation to get me to cease calling in patient allegations of abuse. Sometimes these attacks were in written email and copied to human resources other times they were tacit and implied.

As a result of concerns about the safety of patients in this particular program, a disability rights advocate was called by a legal guardian to help advocate for their child. The child was on my caseload and the legal guardian respected my work and my ethics. The legal guardian broached her intent to me prior to calling and I encouraged her to do so. For this reason, she asked the disability-rights advocate to meet with me personally and alone when she was on site.

The disability-rights advocate asked the CEO if she could meet privately with me. As a result, I was summoned to the front desk, where I was met by both the CEO and the advocate. Walking to that front desk, which was located across the campus, I was quite nervous. I did not trust the CEO to allow this interview to take place unimpeded. Indeed, the CEO was part of the Trifecta of Abuse, and I knew she would do her best to stifle any information from going beyond the facility walls.

When I arrived at the front desk, the CEO introduced us and advised me that advocate was a "good friend of ours" and has "been here many times." The CEO repeated multiple times that the advocate was a friend and reminded me they were close. This sort of tacit intimidation did not go unnoticed. The advocate and I were then guided to a conference room and the door was closed as the CEO walked out. The advocate then got up and unplugged the phone in the room and sat back down.

She began by stating she did not trust the CEO and that they were absolutely not friends. She expressed that she believed the CEO listened through the phone system to conversations that took place around the facility. She then began to ask about the program, and I let her know many of the things that went on that were dangerous to the residents. Being able to share this with someone externally was cathartic. It felt like I had an ally and that my concerns were being validated.

I became very close with the disability-rights advocate who subsequently began to frequent Agency Two. We worked collaboratively and advocated both internally and externally for the best interests of the patients. Eventually, she was involved in several patient cases and was on the agency's grounds with increased frequency. It also became increasingly evident to the CEO that I was providing salient information to help the disability-rights advocate be even more effective.

The advocate and I began to notice an emerging pattern of retaliation against me shortly after the advocate was on grounds. Indeed, her visits and the retaliation against me were always in immediate temporal proximity. For example, the morning after one of her late-day visits, I was written up and accused of attempting to unilaterally discharge a patient. As many healthcare professionals know, in an in-patient facility a social worker cannot unilaterally discharge a patient. This decision must come in the form of a discharge order made by a physician. The allegation was utterly specious, but the attempt at retaliation and intimidation was abundantly clear.

As a result of the increased scrutiny of my work and the thematic breaches of the agency's fiduciary responsibilities, I decided it was time to progressively escalate my concerns to corporate compliance at our corporate headquarters. I did not, however, make this decision lightly. I attempted to resolve my concerns internally, and on multiple occasions, to no avail. Meanwhile, the incidents mounted, and the environment became increasingly dangerous to patients and staff.

In fact, on a beautiful Friday afternoon I stood outside speaking to one of my direct supervisors. He was a competent and ethical psychologist who had tried to improve the agency but was unable to penetrate the corporate protection that surrounded our CEO. The agency was making money – a lot of it – so many transgressions by the CEO were either ignored or forgiven. This psychologist supervisor and I were talking about my eventual fate of being terminated as soon as they could find a reason that might stick and would not be actionable if I sued them. We discussed the increased scrutiny of everything I did and the retaliation I was experiencing. The leadership in my department all seemed to like me and many of them told me about discussions that were occurring behind my back.

My immediate supervisors all did what they could to protect me and they supported what I was advocating for. With only one exception, they just didn't do it themselves. I can remember telling this particular supervisor, on that late Friday afternoon, that I was okay with my fate because, "I don't understand how anyone with a conscience can work here." He agreed and subsequently left for the day. The next day, he sent an email with his immediate resignation. In his resignation he cited some of the concerns I had broached time and again. He concluded by saying that that it was only a matter of time before a serious incident occurred. Indeed, he was sadly correct. There were multiple patient deaths under the leadership of the CEO. The director who resigned never returned to the agency, distancing his name and his reputation from the substandard care and ill treatment of patients found here.

As mentioned, after exhausting all internal mechanisms at Agency Two, I decided it was time to write to corporate compliance. My letter was just under ten pages and included nearly 40 pages of supporting documentation. As you have to be, this particular piece of advocacy was incredibly thorough and detailed. Indeed, any formal letter like this needs to be factually accurate (with supporting documentation) and void of personal feelings and emotion.

When I referenced an incident in my letter, I provided documentation and reports, especially if they were contradictory, as they often were. For example, an email from the risk manager would cite "no restraints yesterday," but other documentation would clearly illustrate there were restraints that day and that the risk manager's email was factually incorrect. In Agency Two, incidents were often kept from key staff and kept from external regulators. We were frequently told to not document incidents in the patient record because the patient record is discoverable. As mentioned above, we were told to document them on incident reports for corporate only.

My letter was extensive, accusatory, and well document-ed. By way of illustration, some of the accusations in my letter included instances of the CEO:

- circumventing our fiduciary responsibility to protect patients in our care.
- failing to comply with mandated reporting responsibilities.
- tactics thematic with harassment, intimidation, and constructive dismissal.
- violating labor laws.
- promoting an environment where sexual assault of residents was possible.
- mixing adult and adolescent patients for programming.
- not properly providing salient information, such as physical holds, to key staff.
- the frequent use of chemical restraints.

Naturally, each allegation had to be backed up with very specific details and documentation from as many sources as possible. The advocate/whistleblower who wants to put his or her name to a corporate compliance complaint must make it as detailed as possible to make it meaningful. When you provide dates, times, people involved, incident reports, inspec-tion reports, meeting minutes and notes, emails, etc. it becomes increasingly difficult for profane figureheads to deny or dismiss a complaint. You have to take the reader through a timeline of what you have experienced with fact and very few personal thoughts, beliefs, and feelings. In this particular case, I provided a copy of my letter to corporate compliance, the CEO, and our on-site human resources director. I also submitted it late in the day so I could go home shortly after.

The retaliatory actions to my letter came in close temporal proximity. Indeed, the very next day the director of Human Resources met with my supervisor and me to discuss my unfavorable and immediate schedule change. Suddenly, the schedule I had worked for more than six months was no longer meeting the needs of the CEO. I let HR know that I believed this to be retaliatory as there was no benefit to myself or the patients in my new schedule. The HR director flatly laid out the information, but it was obvious it was only because she was told to and not that she thought it was the right thing to do. In fact, in a meeting with my supervisor he reports that the Director of HR told him, "This isn't going to end well because Kyle knows what he's doing." My supervisor later helped with reasons for me to stick with my usual schedule and he helped to justify that my original schedule was better for meeting the needs of our patients and families, because it actually was.

My supervisor was so supportive and ethical that he was subsequently demoted for refusing to participate in retaliatory actions against me. The CEO hired another supervisor for our department and told her I was trouble and had to be the first to go. Initially, this new supervisor was on board and immediately sought to document anything she could find to terminate me.

My new supervisor sat in on my meetings with patients looking for something she could write up to discipline me. She participated in group sessions that I led. In the end, she did not find anything viable and actually applauded the work I was doing, particularly under such close scrutiny. After a few weeks of watching my performance closely, she asked my old supervisor for feedback. He told her that I was not the problem with the agency. Privately, through emails between her and others, she fought to keep me in vain.

Sadly, nothing improved in my absence. In fact, months later, similar to my prior supervisor, the director who terminated me walked out of a meeting and quit her job on the spot. Much like the last person, she too did not want her name and reputation associated with the agency any longer and came to the belief that she was powerless to improve the place.

Imagine what could have happened if the entire department acted as a collective unit and refused to participate in things that were going on there. Not one member of my department told me that speaking up about the problems at Agency Two was wrong or that I was going too far with my concerns. They were all in agreement that things were happening there were wrong. In fact, it seemed only that the Trifecta, and a few of their ally abusers, believed I was wrong in my advocacy.

———

Chapter 8

In Conclusion

I can assure you that the literature about the consequences to the whistleblower, and the subsequent impact on the whistleblower's mental health, are very real. I experienced many of these consequences in the most profound way, and I would be remiss to deny them here. That said, the consequences and long-term impact on patients because people do not speak up is very real as well. We should never give up on victims of abuse in institutions or other substandard organizations.

Sometimes you truly do not know if you are making a difference. On the surface, it may appear that nothing changes. Meaningful change takes time and persistent advocacy. That said, understand that you are not privy to all that goes on behind closed doors and that you may never know if something you did made a difference in the long-term. Additionally, whistleblowing is frequently a progressive escalation of concerns. This progressive escalation does not always cease when one leaves an agency, and whistleblowing does not end when you walk out the agency for the last time. In fact, sometimes your day of departure is just the beginning of the process.

Additionally, it is equally important to note that many prior whistleblowers, myself included, do not regret blowing the whistle. Rothschild and Miethe (1999) report, "Given the personal and financial devastation that we heard from so many whistleblowers, it may surprise one to learn that 90% of the whistleblowers in our sample said that they would still report misconduct if they had a chance to do things all over again" (Rothschild and Miethe, 1999, p. 121). They further explain, "through the suffering they have endured—but never anticipated before their disclosure—they have come to see themselves as exceedingly moral. They have distanced themselves from what they now see as the corruption of their former employer, and many begin to see themselves as possessing extraordinary integrity that they now bring to their endeavors" (Rothschild and Miethe, 1999, p. 121). Indeed, the whistleblower is not always relegated to a life of despair on the heels of an abruptly ended career. Whistleblowers can endure and reinvent themselves both personally and professionally. Whistleblowing does not have to be how your story ends.

Agency One

Many of the problems that plagued Agency One began with the CEO. Indeed, at Agency One, the CEO was the head of the snake. In his very short tenure of approximately two years, he terminated dozens of great people, some of whom I keep in contact with to this day. I knew that many of the problems at

Agency One would have been alleviated without the current CEO being there.

I remember a meeting with a corporate clinical representative and our internal Risk Manager. I had watched many people who spoke up disappear but realized this was my chance to describe some of the substandard care, fraud, and negligent care that was promulgated at the agency under the direction of the current CEO. For this reason, I took the opportunity to speak up and provide details of both abuse and fraud. I provided specific patient records where this fraud and abuse were indicated. I offered copies of examples that I had brought with me to the meeting, but corporate clinical representative replied "I'll find it" in the patient records herself. It is my understanding that she did pull patient records after the meeting and met with the CEO to discuss her findings. In addition, in this meeting, I reiterated my refusal to participate in violations of law such as refusal to solicit patients for testimonials.

Fewer than 30 days later, the CEO entered my office with the Risk Manager. With a shaky voice he told me that I had "one foot in the door and one foot out and he had decided to let me go." He explained that my termination would be effective immediately and his hand shook as he handed me an index card with the corporate Human Resources phone number on it so that I could inquire about COBRA benefits. He then left the Risk Manager in my office to show me out. When he left, he fired a nurse who worked in my department and had done an excellent job documenting the substandard care the agency was providing under his failed leadership. She had a wealth of documentation of her attempts to resolve the issues of substandard care with him directly. There are also two very salient things about my brief termination meeting that should be noted here.

The reference to my having one foot in and one foot out related to the fact that I was being recruited by a competitor to oversee programs at a hospital in a neighboring town. I had declined that opportunity and made the CEO aware of it. He decided, however, that was the narrative he would portray to me and to corporate. He was aware that I had already told him and corporate that I had declined the offer.

Second, he terminated my position when our internal Director of Human Resources was on maternity leave. Prior to her leave, she assured me that he could not terminate me because I had not been written up or given progressive discipline for anything. Simply, there was no documentation of anything that I had done wrong. That said, I was not shocked that he acted in her absence. This young man possessed no significant work experience and was perhaps the most incompetent leader I have ever worked with. I knew that removing him from his position would be far easier from outside the agency.

This organization had already begun a downward spiral under the leadership of this CEO. His terminations rarely included proper documentation, and any good leader would know this presents a serious liability for an agency and vicarious liability to a parent company that repeatedly allows this to continue. In fact, I learned from a local attorney that there were more than a dozen EEOC complaints already filed against the facility under his failed leadership. Moreover, many believed he was both sexist and racist, and he did not possess the skill set to hide undertones of this in meetings, so there were multiple witnesses to his inappropriate and actionable comments.

Additionally, once I was gone from Agency One, I was advised that they had just settled a case with a Nurse Practitioner who had originally participated in billing fraud, but then was terminated when she declined to continue her participation in the fraud. Indeed, I had evidence of this fraud, which I provided to the FBI.

As noted in prior chapters, the agency had been cited by the state licensing agency, on multiple occasions, for patient rights to care in a safe setting. In multiple reports the agency was cited due to their persistent failure to mitigate elopement risks from their locked units. Additionally, there were two suicide attempts under this CEO's leadership in which the doctor's prescribed level of supervision was not followed by the staff.

Multiple good people working within this agency continued to provide me updates on major incidents so that I could report them to the state licensing agents, and I did so on multiple occasions. Each email I sent to the state had a progressively escalating tone. Much like in other agencies, I acquired copies of inspection reports and used those to show compounded problems and an increased call to action. I also made sure that the parent company's corporate compliance was aware of every state visit and the thematic problems detailed in the citations.

Although they are usually available through public records requests, and in some states online, I am aware that most staff in agencies do not ever see hospital inspection reports or corrective action plans. In some instances, selective information is shared because it relates to something that the agency had agreed to improve when they were cited for a wrongdoing. I heartily believe that it is important for employees to know what inspection reports reveal about a facility. Indeed, the more I reported about Agency One, the more the citations continued to mount.

For the reasons punctuated above, I thought it important to write to my team at Agency One to illustrate a chronology of events, to show the truth behind my abrupt departure, and to highlight the mounting citations the agency was receiving. My goals were multifarious. Foremost, I wanted people to be aware of the citations and the agency that their own reputations were affiliated with. I also wanted people to be aware of all the behind-the-scenes retaliation that happened within the leadership team. I also knew that my letter would be shared within the broader mental health community outside the agency. Lastly, I also knew that reaching out would encourage more people to share information with me so that I could continue to advocate, and I knew the more people who told me things, the less likely people would be terminated for talking because it would make the talkers difficult to find.

As usual, the letter had to be very specific and detailed. While working at Agency One, I had created a packet of information, so I was able to be specific with dates of incidents, meetings, and inspection reports. I quoted from notes, meetings, inspection reports, and people involved in leadership meetings.

The letter was 18 pages in length. There were several sections to my letter where I detailed my experiences, and they were:

- Background.
- Retaliatory leadership and lies.
- Refusal to participate in unethical and illegal activity.
- In-patient program
- Out-patient program.

In this letter I cautioned:

"When confronted about problematic areas that require a decision from the CEO, [name] is unable to stay on task, becomes impulsive, loses control, or simply walks out of meetings. All of you have probably witnessed this firsthand. For this reason, the concerns raised by my predecessor, and those raised by my successor, will continue to fall into his incapable hands and the problems will continue to recur."

In addition to the cautionary words woven throughout my letter, I describe the lamentable quandary and moral dilemma that would be a recurring theme in multiple agencies throughout my career:

"For all staff, however, there still exists a moral dilemma between staying to help the patients and propping up a false and inept leader. Please know that I truly understand the difficulty in speaking up against the thematic problems at [Agency One]. As noted on the paragraphs and pages above, when I spoke up I was immediately subject to harassment, intimidation, and constructive dismissal tactics. When those surreptitious tactics failed to work, I was terminated without cause and in direct retaliation for me reporting and refusing to participate in what I continue to assert are illegal practices. I know you have all seen the same intimidating tactics promulgated on countless other employees, who each spoke up to make things better, without even a feigned interest from [parent company]. I regret that has been the case and that [parent company] continues to align with [CEO] retaliatory, impulsive, and linear management style. This is particularly true considering what a great facility [Agency One] can be under competent leadership."

My plan worked and my letter was widely circulated and became a marketing nightmare for the Agency One. In addition, as hoped for, information started to flow about wrongdoings at the facility. In some instances, pictures of things such as expired and moldy food served to patients also flowed.

As a result, visits from state inspectors became more frequent and the consequences increasingly severe. They include:

[Date 1] visit. Cited for excessive elopements and patient safety issues (attached).

[Date 2] visit. This visit led to a 30-page report of citations.

[Date 3 – five-day visit] leading to them currently being downgraded to operating on a temporary license. This visit also led to a 69-page report of citations by Department of Health (DHH).

The Chief Executive Officer (CEO) of Agency One was one of the most incompetent leaders I ever worked for. He did not possess the skill set for introspection and could not lead without someone from our corporate headquarters directly telling him what do to. In fact, he called them frequently for direction on normal day-to-day operational issues. Similarly, he did not possess the skill set to allow his reports the ability to govern their departments without his constant myopic meddling. This is a CEO who quite literally would spend his afternoon picking up litter that had blown across the parking lot while his hospital was falling apart around him. As a result of ongoing inspections, concerns, and his inability to govern through the agency's frequent receipt of corrective action plans, the CEO of Agency One was terminated by the parent company just 10 months after I was. His failed leadership was simply unable to withstand the barrage of site visits and agency citations.

———

In an ironic twist, the CEO I liked from Agency Three had taken over as interim CEO at the facility in the neighboring town to Agency One that I had previously declined. Knowing there was a competent interim CEO there made it far more palpable and I took an interim position there as well.

Agency Two

On one sunny afternoon, I was summoned to Human Resources at Agency Two. In my heart I knew that this was the day because it came shortly after my second formal letter to corporate compliance, and I had also filed a Medicaid fraud complaint just days prior. Indeed, I was progressively escalating my concerns and the agency was becoming increasingly concerned about the impact I might have.

I walked across campus to the HR office and was met by my direct supervisor and the Director of HR. I was handed a document explaining that I was being terminated effective immediately. I asked the Director of HR for a copy of the document and she stepped out of the office to make a copy. As soon as she left the room, my direct supervisor looked over at me and mouthed the words "I am sorry." My direct supervisor and HR then walked me to my office to collect my car keys and a pack of mints I had on my desk. There were no other personal belongings in my office, so there was no need for a dramatic exit. I knew exactly what this show was intended to accomplish, so my goal was intended to minimize the drama as much as possible.

It also helped that for the previous three days they had me training my own replacement under the guise that the agency was hiring a much-needed extra person. What the Trifecta of Abuse was not aware of was that my direct supervisor, my replacement, and I had met together and discussed the fact that I was being terminated soon and the new person would be my replacement. In their haste to terminate me as quickly as possible, the Trifecta failed to look into my replacement's background fully and they ended up replacing me with a woman whose moral compass was much the same as my own. Although I had no plans to cease advocating for the patients at the program, it was nice that I had been replaced by someone who shared the same moral and ethical beliefs about patient care. Indeed, she too was a tireless advocate for patients. They terminated her a few months later.

As I mentioned at the start of this chapter and throughout this book, the consequence to whistleblowers punctuated in the research are very real. With respect to my life after Agency Two, they became painful and profound.

Upon being terminated from Agency Two, I began a two-year stretch of being either barely employed or unemployed. I began to isolate and stay at home. I struggled with sleep in the evenings and then would sleep most of the day. I applied for countless jobs and went on several interviews. In the interviews I was sometimes asked about the whistleblower situation at my last agency because it had made its way into the media and my name was mentioned in the press. It was a very emotional time.

I recall one job interview for a position that I really wanted. The interview was before an entire department and one of the directors asked about the situation at my old facility. Someone on the panel chimed in and said that she had read a lot about it, was familiar with the agency, and I was absolutely in the right and shut the question down. Tears welled up in my eyes because the validation of doing the right thing was witnessed by someone in the field. I did not get that job or several others I applied for.

Even worse, when I lowered my expectations and applied for a position I was overqualified for, a director in one interview stated, "You are way overqualified for this position. What are your true motives here?" My motive was to work and earn a living.

About two years later, I lost my struggle with the foreclosure proceedings on my modest home. As the foreclosure process was happening, I sank into an even deeper depression and con-templated suicide. I loved the house so much and had a very personal attachment to it and so I thought of ways to die in it. I vacillated from depressed and suicidal to understanding that I could reinvent myself after I picked up the pieces. Indeed, this milestone, however painful, did not have to be the final chapter of my life.

I had a few supportive friends who reached out throughout

the process. Others did not understand. I reached out to a family member who did not take my calls and then did not speak to me for three more years. We were once very close and several years after not speaking this relationship has since improved. Another family member became angry at the consequences of my blowing the whistle. That relationship never recovered.

Parallel to this process, I continued to advocate for the patients trapped in that facility and continued my progressive escalation of concerns. I closely followed each inspection report and took each piece of documentation about the ongoing problems that plagued this facility as a new opportunity to both advance and control the narrative. I continued speaking regularly with reporters and both suggested and prompted them to explore multiple avenues of concern, taking careful efforts to ensure that different outlets were given different nuggets of information to explore further. They all did.

I kept up to date on abuses and problems in the facility. I let reporters know where they could find additional information and who else might be willing to speak to them. For example, one media outlet wished to explore, in greater detail, incidents of child abuse. As you might surmise, HIPAA prevents healthcare workers from giving out patient information to the media, but I was able to funnel the representatives of the outlet to lawyers whom disability rights had funneled patients to. I could not provide patient names, but I could provide the names of their lawyers so that they could make their own informed decisions about participating.

In addition to the media outlets, I was progressively escalating information with law enforcement entities as well. Prior to leaving the agency, I filed a complaint with the Centers for Medicare & Medicaid Services (CMS) about billing fraud. My continued advocacy also included providing documentation to a law enforcement lieutenant from the Office of the Attorney General of the state in which the facility was operating.

Sharing parts of my whistleblower packet of information with these offices eventually led to a face-to-face meeting with four officials from the state's Attorney General's office. In preparing for these meetings, I organized all of my documentation in different binders and put them in chronological order. Since I spent so much time reviewing the timeline of events, I had a profound mastery of these materials. These officials asked questions and reviewed documentation and eventually made the determination to bump the case up to the Federal Bureau of Investigation (FBI).

Similarly, the FBI met with me and reviewed the documents as well. Again, I had four people asking me questions for almost four hours. As you might surmise, every assertion you make to the FBI about wrongdoing needs to be backed up and corroborated with documentation and other sources. I provided the FBI with a witness list and shared what I believed each person would say. Over the course of the next few months, the FBI met with all the individuals I broached with them.

In the months after meeting with the FBI, I endured multiple instances of being followed. Two instances are particularly notable, because they were noticed by someone other than myself. If I had noticed it, I would have probably dismissed it as paranoia. As well, the woman who replaced me and also spoke up about wrongdoing reported similar instances in which she believes she too was being followed. She also met with the Attorney General's Office and then the FBI.

In the first instance, I was at an event being held at a hotel where I was staying multiple nights. One afternoon a friend of mine came and asked to borrow my car to go get some food. When he returned with my keys, he threw them on the desk and stated, "You are being followed." I was surprised to hear this and asked why he thought so. He explained that there was a man sitting in a car near mine and when he pulled out, the car followed him. He further explained that he was suspicious about being followed so he went down several side streets, and through a residential area, and the car continued to follow him. He then pulled into a nearby fast-food restaurant and when he got out of the car, the car following him took off. Perhaps they realized they were following my car, but not following me.

The other notable instance occurred when I was visiting my mother. A friend picked me up for dinner and we went to a nearby restaurant to eat. On the way home, as she drives down my mother's street to drop me off, she casually mentioned that the car behind us was following us for a while now. I told her the story about the friend who had borrowed my car. As I was finishing the story she pulled into my mother's driveway. The car following us stopped across the street and just waited. It became quite obvious the car was, in fact, following us. The car parked across from my mother's house, facing the wrong direction, with the engine still running. My friend said, "I want to know who this is now" and pulled out to follow the car. It abruptly took off and we lost it.

To this day I don't know why I was being followed, but I felt it worth noting here. Law firms do hire private investigators to help collect information that might help their cases. If you are engaged in litigation, or people think you might be in the future, an investigator could be looking into you and trying to gather information to help out the other side.

About two-and-a-half years after my last day at Agency Two, I got full-time contractor job on a military base. The background check was grueling, and I had to write and rewrite, the story of what happened at Agency Two. It took several rounds and progressively more detailed questions, including naming all of the agents I spoke to about Agency Two, before they deemed me able to work there.

After just a few months at this new job, my whistleblower PTSD actually became more obvious to me. In one situation, I had to advocate for a patient to receive treatment outside our clinic, with a commanding officer. I had promised myself that, unless it was a life-or-death situation, I would just keep my head down and do my job so that I did not get fired and lose so much again. In this particular case, I worried the commander would be reluctant to send the patient, but I believed it was in his best interest. I made my case and the commander agreed. In another case, I was nervous to approach a friendly doctor, who I believed had misdiagnosed a patient. Again, this was not a life-or-death situation, so I was hesitant and anxious, but the difference in diagnosis would have meant a different medi-cation regimen and course of a different course of treatment. I broached the issue with this particular doctor and stated why I believed the diagnosis was incorrect and she promptly agreed. This position restored my faith in the field. The director of this clinic, and all the staff working in it, made the people we treated their top priority and governed themselves accordingly.

Even while I was working, the FBI was meeting with people and preparing for what they might do, I continued to speak to and provide information to reporters. I continued to expand and control the narrative of Agency Two. I worked with others to ensure there was documentation in the public domain about both prior and ongoing incidents at the facility.

Over the course of the two to three-plus years following my departure from Agency Two, the state would frequent the facility, cite them repeatedly for wrongdoing, enforce a correc-tive action plan, and take no further action against the facility. Throughout the next two to three years, the agency would be cited by the state for repetitive breaches of nonmaleficence and law. I did my best to work with others and ensure each incident documented by the state made it into the public domain and could not for the life of me understand how repeated breaches of the same law did not result in the state licensing agency doing more. Then I remembered my conversation with the one agent who stated they were afraid of the agency with deep pockets suing them.

Throughout this process I also cannot begin to tell you how many times I heard from naysayers that "nothing will ever change" and listened to others question "is it worth it?" Surely, national accrediting bodies and licensing agents did not care enough to shut it down and so one might wonder why I persisted. Again, my penchant for protecting people from abuse has always remained unwavering.

Stories continued to proliferate though the community and the narrative that plagued Agency Two flooded the public domain. The news stories, each grounded in fact and supported with substantial documentation, caused a drop in the program census. Each story punctuated the narrative of an abusive agency disinterested in changing their ways. Eventually this caused a significant drop in census, and revenue, and eventually caused the termination of the CEO.

Indeed, the Trifecta was penetrated and one individual in the Trifecta was removed. Shortly after, the agency did its best to project the image of a new CEO and a fresh start. Except nothing really had changed and, with the help of others, the story of the children trapped in this horrible place continued to be told. Eventually, after nearly four years of persistence, the agency closed due to their inability to raise the program census and the continued decline of their revenue. Indeed, the news stories dried up referrals and kept the census too low to continue operation. Agency Two was now so damaged that it was no longer financially viable.

I will never forget the day I learned of Agency Two's closing. I was sitting in a lovely two-bedroom apartment just minutes from the beach. The apartment was barely furnished, as I was working and rebuilding my life and reinvent my career.

I began purchasing bits and pieces of things as I put my life back together. One sunny weekend afternoon, I received a call from the disability-rights advocate who I met with in that conference room more than three years prior. We never lost touch and we never stopped advocating for these children. When she explained to me that Agency Two was closing in the next week because they could not increase their low census, tears welled up in my eyes. This was a great victory, but it was a victory with profound consequences.

Agency Two was unable to increase the program census because the media stories dominated the narrative about the agency. I cried because I knew that they were closing because we kept the narrative alive and insisted on telling the stories of those children. They were not closing because any of the unfaithful angels were taking strong action and shutting it down. It was a long time coming, but now it was here.

Agency Three

Agency Three was another residential treatment program for teens. The program had gotten into trouble with the state before I got there and was almost shut down by the state. Multiple staff members were indicted for having sexual relations with the teenage residents. The agency was caught covering up of abuse, fraud, and sexual incidents. The state had investigated, and staff were criminally charged. The incidents were widely publicized, and the program census declined to just a handful of residents.

The parent company was committed to keeping the program open. They hired a new CEO and gave him resources to do whatever it took to improve the reputation of the program. The CEO brought me on board to help with this turnaround and I committed to one year at the facility. As mentioned in prior chapters, the turning around of Agency Three was serious. The CEO was one who was not willing to cover up any incidents of any kind and had a lot of integrity. Indeed, he had a penchant for strength-based care and was supportive of any effort to clean the place up. When I arrived at this program, of just over 50 beds, they had a program census in the low teens.

The corporate owners of this program also stated a goal to improve the program. In fact, one member from corporate who visited the facility frequently during my tenure admitted that the company had not paid enough attention to the facility because it was bringing in money and was always full. He acknowledged it was a mistake and that he wanted the place turned around.

Throughout the year, we purged staff who were not into a strength-based model of care. We tried to promote a trauma informed environment. When incidents arose, we reported them honestly to the state and provided copies of the videos from the incidents. In turn, the state started to trust us again and the referrals came in with increased frequency. By the end of my year there, they were ready to create a substance abuse unit and an assessment and diagnostic unit.

Sadly, shortly after my one year was completed, the CEO was also changed. It was not long before the program degenerated into old problems and was closed for good.

Agency Four

The problems I noticed at Agency Four were the direct result of an inept leadership team. Included in that description is my direct supervisor, but in fairness I always saw him as more of a lackey. It was my belief that the lackey could be a decent supervisor if the people around him wanted him to be. He knew the subject matter of his job and was good with external constituencies but lacked the ability to stand up to people and do the right thing, always. Others aptly characterized him as a chameleon based on his ability to be in a room and say whatever people in that room wanted him to say, and then contradict himself later in a different room where people wanted to hear something different. I actually believed he would do the right thing if that was what he was told to do, but I had no respect for his lack of moral compass and his willingness to allow substandard care to permeate throughout the organization.

The ironic thing about Agency Four was that that I obtained my job there when the agency decided to lay off its entire clinical team to enter a contract with a local hospital to provide clinical services there. When they laid people off, they did not hire them all back and so I got a position there. Just over two years later, the contract was abruptly cancelled, and the entire team was laid off and then rehired under the agency again. In that transition they did not hire everyone back and I was one of the people not hired back. It was a very interesting way to get rid of people who did not agree with what they were doing. Some have said that the original contract with the local hospital was

Medicaid fraud and that is why it ended, but I have no evidence of that.

What I do know, however, is that we were told by the lackey to bill for every interaction with a patient. He described interactions where we might find ourselves walking across campus and a resident stops us and we have a brief conversation with them as a billable interaction. In followup, a colleague and I called Medicaid to explain our contract with the agency and to inquire if such interactions were ever billable under some CPT code we might not have learned about. Our billing forms that we sent to the hospital billing department did not have the actual Current Procedural Terminology (CPT) code on them. There was brief individual and individual therapy. No code and no timeframes were specified. So, to ensure our beliefs were correct, we called and asked. The answer, as you probably imagined, was no. we cannot bill for such brief interactions. We were both then chastised by the woman who took our call and reminded that any licensed therapist who puts his or her name to such a bill would be guilty of the fraud, not the agency and not the person who directed us to do it. Our contract with the hospital ended two months after this call.

When I left Agency Four, I had already compiled my packet. This packet was quite extensive as I was gathering evidence for what I had hoped would be convincing the leadership team to fix problems within this agency. Agency Four was a nonprofit that was governed by a board of trustees. It was my steadfast belief that the board of trustees had no idea what was going on in the agency. The board was comprised of a group of wealthy do-gooders who believed they were helping orphaned children by providing them a better life. I don't think that they realized how purposefully unsafe the agency was for kids under the current administrative team or the population they were serving.

Since my belief in Agency Four was that the board of trustees were not aware of the problems, and the problems were isolated to the management team, I sat down to write the full board a letter. In writing to a board of an agency, it is always important to remember to redact patient information if you endeavor to include such detail. As always, I had my packet of information to support any assertions that I was about to make. My assertions of the problems in Agency Four were multifarious and were punctuated throughout a nearly twenty-page letter that included more than five hundred pages of supporting documentation. Indeed, well over a full ream of paper was being prepared for each trustee.

Knowing that a packet this large would likely be overwhelming to read, I included a cover letter that bullet-pointed the information contained in the full packet. In my cover letter I reminded the trustees of their fiduciary responsibility and their vicarious liability for what transpires in the agency they govern. I bullet-pointed every point that was expanded upon in my letter and the ream of supporting documentation. My last day at this program was in October and the packet arrived via express mail to each of the trustee's homes just days before Christmas.

When I began this book talking about having no idea what impact you may be having, it was to encourage whistleblowers to keep going even when it looks like nothing will change. Agency Four truly punctuates this point. I continued my advocacy here because I believed, and had the documentation to show, that children were not being treated well here, and my documentation illustrated a clear path of blame to the leadership team's actions and behaviors. The full context of my package to the trustees was simply to make this central point.

When my package arrived at the trustees' homes on time for Christmas, the initial response was to attack. I received a cease-and-desist letter from their lawyer, and some of the people I knew there became afraid to talk to me. To this day, I have no idea what was said to anyone about my packet as the information from the agency stopped flowing to me.

For about a month after my packet was sent, it looked like nothing would change at Agency Four. Then over the course of the next few months, the leadership team began dropping from the facility. It did not happen in one fell swoop, but one by one they were each replaced. I do not know if members of the leadership team quit, were fired, or were constructively dismissed. To this day, I really do not know if my letter did it or if something else happened at the agency to cause the board to change Agency Four's leadership team. If the board paid closer attention because of my letter, they would have easily seen the patterns recur. I imagine pieces of my letter ended up in personnel files and at least contributed to a change in leadership.

The only person from the leadership team at Agency Four who remained was the chameleon. I am guessing he probably saw the shifting tide, after the first few members of the leader-ship team disappeared, and sold the rest of the team out to save himself, just as he did the residents and his own department. That said, I am confident he remained and did what he was told, and I hope that is to do ethical work.

Agency Five

Agency Five was an outpatient hospital program that served as a good example of what can happen when leadership listens. This agency was part of a hospital system that struggled finan-cially, but also represents a place where I met some of the best doctors and therapists in the industry.

For a brief period of time at Agency Five, I worked for a leader who micromanaged her people, including her insisting on proofreading and signing every letter that went out. I was in charge of a grant program that was administered by the Youth Services Commission in the state. I was recommended for this position by members of the Youth Services Commission itself.

The program included sending out a form letter every time a youth missed a therapy appointment. My direct supervisor at the time required that she co-sign these missed-appointment letters even though the only thing that ever changed on them was the date of the missed appointment. I was actually fine with her co-signing. The problem started when she held on to the letter for days, and sometimes more than a week, before she allowed them to be mailed or faxed.

One afternoon I received a call from a probation officer who I had worked closely with in the past and had a great working relationship with. She questioned the delay in a letter I was supposed to send her for court. She stated, "What happened to you? You used to be so prompt and good at this." I explained the letter was done and in the process of being co-signed by my boss. In followup, I wrote my boss an email explaining the delays she is causing are now impacting our relationship with salient people who can impact our grant. I provided three examples of letters that I had given her and the dates I provided them to her and the date she returned them. I reminded her that she gave them back after they were due in court, meaning we were late in getting them to probation and court on time. I concluded with asking if there was anything that I could do to help expedite the letter co-signing process. Again, I didn't have a problem with the process. Everyone can use a proofreader for things that will be read by others. My problem was the delays it was causing and the potential damage to the program's reputation.

Much to my surprise, I was summoned to a meeting the next day with my supervisor at the time, Human Resources, and the Director of Psychiatry. The Director of Psychiatry was well known as a bully, and her boss, the vice president of Psychiatry, was rumored to have a temper as well. The VP of Psychiatry was not present for this meeting.

The meeting began with the Director of Psychiatry asserting "Your email to your supervisor was borderline insubordination." She continued, "We are moving you to a different unit effective immediately" and explained I would be assigned different patients. I could not believe that my email triggered such a response. I was furious inside. I calmly replied, "There is no such thing as borderline insubordination. There is subordination or no subordination, and I will take time to think about it and let you know my response." Indeed, this was my way of asserting "addendum to follow" and to buy myself time to process what was transpiring. There was no paperwork in this meeting, so I had nowhere to write my key phrase, "addendum to follow," so I verbally asserted it. The bully asserted back, "The decision has been made." I continued to be floored by the idea that my benign email had triggered such a response. At that point, I looked at HR and asked, "So there is no appeals procedure?" HR replied, "Well, there is precedent that you can be moved and reassigned immediately." To which I questioned back, "Legally challenged precedent, or you did it before and got away with it?" The bully immediately asserted, "The decision has been made" and she abruptly ended the meeting.

I went home that day and wrote a formal grievance letter. The letter was just under ten pages long. In the letter I expanded on the dates and times that I had put in my email to include other documents as well. I stuck to the facts. I was very concrete and explained things like, "I gave my boss the letter for co-sign on xx day and received it back on xx day." If the letter was not to probation on time for a court date, I included the court date as well.

I was very upset with this entire situation because I was hired to run a program under a grant for a specific population that I had worked hard to become an expert at. Now this was being stripped from me and I was going to be forced to work with a population I was not hired to work with and had little to no experience with. I also knew that there was a high likelihood that they would lose the grant if I was not involved in the running of the program. It was very clear to me that they were trying to make me miserable so that I would quit. Indeed, I believed I was being constructively discharged and I included that in my letter as well.

I had the next day off and I took my letter to an employment lawyer to review. I was glad that I did. The lawyer reminded me that any letter or documentation requested by a probation officer is an order of the court. He further added that if my supervisor was delaying the letter from getting to the probation officer on time, she was in violation of a court order. I actually had not put that together originally, but her not complying with the law and my stated refusal to participate in it was a protected activity. The lawyer made a few minor editing changes and then said to me, "The best thing that could happen to you is you submit this and get fired and I will take your case on contingency fee." I was floored. I really did not consider getting fired to be the best thing that could happen to me. I actually liked my job. I didn't even wait till the next workday to submit my letter. I submitted it to HR and the Vice President of Psychiatry via email that day. Within hours I received a call from HR explaining that the VP of Psychiatry wanted to speak with me first thing in the morning. I was anxious. I was told that this man had a temper. I just wanted to keep doing the work I had been doing.

Much to my surprise, when I arrived at the VP's office, he

invited me in and took out a legal pad, grabbed his pen, looked at me and asked, "What would make you happy? What do you want to happen?" I told him that I wanted to keep working with the grant program that I was hired for. He then asked if he could move the entire grant program to a different supervisor and have me continue to be involved in running it and working with the same patients. I told him that was fine and that is exactly what happened.

In my first meeting with my new supervisor, he let me know that whatever happened with the other supervisor would not impact anything under his leadership. He used the phrase "tabula rasa" to explain we would be starting with a clean slate. Within the next three months my old supervisor was gone from the hospital. Shortly after, the new director of that unit asked me if I wanted to come back over there. I thanked her and said that I was fine where I was.

The supervisor I was moved under was decent, unassuming, and generally easy to work for. He let me do my job and run the program I was hired to run. After being there a short time, some of my colleagues and I realized that many of us were moved under this department director because it didn't work out for us in other departments. Some were former and short-term directors who were better as therapists and were moved here to continue doing the good therapy that they do. Some of us eventually dubbed the department as the land of the misfits, but it was really the land of some of the best doctors and therapists I have ever worked with. Patients were always priority one. Throughout the next four years my boss and I wrote grants together, completed outcomes studies, and I was generally happy under his leadership. Eventually, I left the hospital to open a private practice in a different state.

Although it was shaky for a moment in Agency Five, I felt compelled to include the experience because it was a testament to what happens when you advocate effectively and an agency eventually does the right thing. Believe it or not, it does sometimes happen.

Chapter Eight

Substantive Change

It is my sincerest hope that this book inspires and informs agents of change. It is with a sad heart for the profession that I continue to read scores of news articles about maltreatment in healthcare settings. While all the stories dot the landscape of those lives impacted, sometimes totally ruined, by the maltreatment, I look at these stories through an additional lens: How is it possible that people, purported to be caring professionals, choose not to speak up?

Similarly, I do not believe healthcare professional's obligations end when they simply report substandard care or maltreatment to one of the accomplices, imposters, or unfaithful angels. There is ample evidence that the people in the accomplice, imposter, and unfaithful angel positions frequently fail to protect people or to take meaningful action. Effective advocates simply cannot rest on these laurels. Until the problem is eliminated, there is always more that can be done.

As noted throughout this book, taking action is not always a fast process, but it is an important process. Failing to act has a long-lasting and profound impact on the lives of the people we are supposed to treat with dignity, compassion, and those we are sworn to protect.

Provider Licensing Boards

Foremost, I believe that there should be more accountability, assigned to individuals who fail to speak up with their respective licensing boards. This is particularly true of licensed professionals who work in healthcare settings that have a history of malfeasance. It continues to mystify me how licensed professionals can go about their daily lives in agencies that do such harm to those they treat.

I do think the healthcare professional's inaction should be actionable with state licensing boards: When a healthcare professional is cited in a corrective action report by a state licensing agency for failing to report or take action on a wrongdoing, this should automatically trigger a licensing board complaint for the individual who failed to act. It is my belief the outcome of this would be at least two-fold. It would encourage more people to speak up. It would also begin to start showing strength in numbers, because the more people who speak up, the harder it would be to retaliate against those who speak up.

Automatic triggering of licensing board complaints when a healthcare professional is named in an agency citation of wrongdoing would mean better protection for people in our care, because this automatic action would make healthcare professionals more compelled to speak up. We know from the research in prior chapters, that some healthcare professionals do not speak up because of fear for their jobs. The loss of one's professional license equates to a loss of identity and, for most, loss of job. I continue to be disturbed by the reality that it is often less damaging for the healthcare worker to remain silent as substandard care continues than it is for them to speak up and refuse to participate in it. This reality needs to be reversed. The automatic triggering of licensing board complaints would serve to help accomplish this.

Additionally, automatic triggering of licensing board complains would likely equate to more people speaking up and refusing to participate in wrongdoing. This would mean ethical practitioners would be less likely to be forced to act unilaterally. Indeed, it is much harder for wrongdoers to penetrate a unified group. If everyone's license is truly put at risk, we are more likely to see people speak out with others against wrongdoing.

The Troubled-Teen Industry

An industry that has evolved considerably over the past few years is commonly referred to as the troubled-teen industry. While there remains considerable abuse in facilities that cater to this demographic, there is an abundance of information and new theories about how to address the problems that plague this industry. Abusive practices have given way to more strength-based techniques and every aspect of the manner in which these programs render consequences and treatment is being examined.

By way of illustration, The Residential Child Care Project at Cornell University endeavors to improve the lives of children living in residential care programs. The Children and Residential Experiences (CARE) program is one of the hallmark programs at Cornell. This model purports to be a "trauma-informed, principle-based, multi-component program designed to enhance the social dynamics in group care settings and help agencies create a living environment that provides developmentally enriching experiences for children in their care" (Holden & Sellars 2019, p. 1).

Greene (1998) offered a strength-based model in which he encourages the avoidance of counterproductive adult reactions to children who become easily frustrated and act out. This strength-based model assumes children want to do well and suggests that the adults need to figure out how they can help. This model is both collaborative and solution focused (Greene 1998). Many programs have adopted a Ross Greene type model over the past twenty years.

One could easily argue that these new methods and techniques are more humane, and, in fact, that would be accurate. There continues to be, however, little or no evidence that the use of residential care leads to more meaningful long-term outcomes. Of course, strength-based programming is better than the punitive alternatives, but the actual outcomes of residential programs for children and adolescents continues to not be measured in a meaningful long-term way. Residential programs, albeit more strength-based and trauma-informed, tend to be very expensive and generally ineffective at the long-term improvement of lives. Additionally, there continues to be abuse in the so called "strength-based and trauma-informed" programs of today.

Invert the Funding

Throughout my career I have always thought that the funding, particularly in our troubled-teen industry, should be inverted, meaning residential treatment programs are very costly and usually well-funded and community-based services are not. Wraparound services and foster care programs are generally quite poorly funded and, therefore, the choice of homes is quite limited. I have always thought we should spend considerably more money on programs to keep kids in the community and out of the abusive troubled-teen residential programs.

The rates paid to foster families for foster care vary considerably by state and can be quite nuanced based on the level of need of the child. As you might surmise, children with complicated medical issues or other issues that require increase levels of care cost more to place in foster care. In 2013, Child Trends did a report breaking down daily rates for children in foster care by state. The Child Trends report found the lowest rate was $7.23 a day in Wisconsin and up to $41 a day in Alaska (DeVooght & Blazey 2013). In addition, foster parents often pay for some of the cost of a foster child's medical care out of their own pocket so this includes paying for medications (prescription and over the counter), co-payments for medical appointments, and medical supplies (Hayes et. al. 2015). In fact, in most states in the U.S., the cost associated with having a child in foster care exceeds the rates paid to families (Rucker 2007, Rickert 2007).

Costs for inpatient care can be close to, or exceed, $1,000 per day (Stensland et. al. 2012). It is estimated that the child and adolescent mental-healthcare industry is more than a $10 billion industry, with inpatient programs making up a full one third of these costs (Strum et. al. 2001). With this level of funding, we could provide quality care to children and adolescents in crisis and need. I would rather see us invert the funding and spend the money before sending someone off to stay in a residential program or hospital.

Increasing the rate paid to foster parents would likely enable foster care to be a more viable option. Additionally, increase reimbursement would likely lead to increased availability of foster homes. I also do not believe increasing the rates would lead to a bunch of people wanting to do it simply because the money is good. More likely, with increased funding, our foster care industry would likely find itself with more placement options and would be able to screen foster parents better to select the best possible placement for a child. In fact, it is frequently reported that there is a shortage of foster homes (Martinez 2000, O'Hanlan 2000) and this shortage is blamed for many of the problems plaguing the foster care industry. Indeed, a shortage of homes has sometimes led to lower standards for securing homes (Indira 1995) or less than optimal placement demographically further away from family (Circelli 2003).

The inverted funding would also serve to improve outpatient

care options. There is often a shortage of options for outpatient care and the outpatient care system is plagued with long wait times. I have personally witnessed, and you may have as well, people decompensate waiting for outpatient appointments and eventually end up hospitalized as a result. The reimbursement rates for outpatient psychotherapy, for example, are low. It isn't until people are hospitalized that the rates increase substantially. While this makes sense on some level because the care in a hospital is supposed to be 24/7 and the patient has access to various licensed professionals, I think slight increases in outpatient reimbursement rates would encourage more people to do it and, therefore, reduce the long waits that lead to the decompensation that puts people in hospitals.

Accreditation

It should be obvious by now that private sector accreditation, such as the accreditation offered by The Joint Commission, has almost nothing to do with ensuring quality care in a healthcare facility. Research conducted by Lam et. al. (2018) revealed no discernable difference in the quality of care in The Joint Commission accredited facilities when compared to state facilities that are not accredited by The Joint Commission. Others have reported serious deficiencies with The Joint Commissions oversight of healthcare facilities and their frequent accreditation of facilities that provide substandard care (Prager 1999, Bodfield and Wabnik 1998, Lieberman 2017, Mole 2017, Hallam 1997, Morning Star 1996).

I should also take a moment to comment here that I do not think these findings about accreditation should stop you from getting medical care if you need it. The cautionary tale here is that you simply should not pick a facility simply because they tout such accreditations and that you cannot count on them to revoke accreditation from bad facilities. Rather, I would ask a nurse or doctor whom you trust where they would send their loved ones for the type of care you require. The trusted nurse or doctor will tell you far more than any diluted gold seal of approval ever will. Additionally, for the purposes of this book and educating whistleblowers, you cannot count on accrediting bodies to stop abuse in institutions, because they never have.

For the general public to get a better understanding of the quality of a healthcare setting, I believe that accreditation should be a highly transparent government process. While the government has also been known to allow substandard care, I do believe they would be less financially incentivized than The Joint Commission, which recently reported revenues in excess of $120 million dollars (McKinney 2010). The Joint Commission makes money even when approving facilities that have a well-documented history of providing poor care. Also, since fees would not be tied to continued accreditation, there would likely be an increased likelihood a facility could lose accreditation without any impact or financial loss on the government-funded, not healthcare-facility-funded, accrediting body.

Additionally, each state should be mandated to have an online database of inspection reports for healthcare facilities. In some states, these reports are actually searchable online, while in other states they are not. In some states the process to obtain these reports is confusing hinders people's ability to make informed decisions about their care. The hospital inspection reports should be readily available online in all states and territories.

I will never understand people who do nothing, or even very little, to protect people who are literally held captive in a healthcare program where abuse transpires. People come into healthcare facilities (medical hospitals, psychiatric units, residential treatment programs, etc.) at a vulnerable time in their lives. I cannot fathom not speaking up when people are mistreated in these facilities, but it happens far too often.

Additional Relief

One of the ways healthcare professionals can help patients is to ensure information about serious wrongdoings of a healthcare facility make it into the public domain. Sometimes public outrage will help rectify problems. If it does not rectify problems, ensuring that the public is aware of abuse and malfeasance will reduce any plausible deniability of agency officials in litigation. Lawyers for patients need to be aware of inspection reports, police call logs, and critical incident reports so that they can help patients who fall victim to thematic problems that a healthcare facility refuses to improve.

As I mentioned throughout this book, healthcare professionals are the healthcare experts. If we make ourselves available for consultation with lawyers, we can serve to help them better understand the nuances of healthcare laws and ethics.

Cascading Transgressions

So much more needs to be done to address the thematic problems of cascading transgressions in healthcare facilities. Cascading transgressions should be a hallmark of ethics discussions in educational programs for healthcare professionals. Transgressions fall within the scope of healthcare ethics and this is often a subject barely broached in healthcare education and training programs.

Lastly, I have worked with so many fantastic healthcare workers over the course of my career. The vast majority of the healthcare workers I have had the privilege of working with carry themselves with professionalism and take their code of ethics and duty to the clients and patients they serve seriously. There are a few healthcare workers that I have worked with who stand out as truly exceptional human beings.

Let this book serve as a call for the ethicists in the field to unite for the good of the clients and patients we serve and to improve the standards of our respective professions. The healthcare profession touches all lives at one point or another and the profession should be led by the most competent and ethical among us.

References

Abdala, N., Li, F., Shaboltas, A. V., Skochilov, R. V., & Krasnoselskikh, T. V. (2016). History of childhood abuse, drinking motives, alcohol use, and sexual risk behavior among STD clinic patients in St. Petersburg, Russia: A cross-sectional study *AIDS and Behavior*, 20(3), 512-522.

Alford, C. F. (2002). Whistleblowers: Broken Lives and Organizational Power. United Kingdom: Cornell University Press.

Armour S. Hospital Watchdog Gives Seal of Approval, Even After Problems Emerge. *Wall Street Journal*. September 8, 2017. Accessed March 24, 2021.

Assad, M. (2007, Dec 16). Crisis brings Kids Peace to a Crossroads: High Number of Restraints, Spike in Police Calls Bring State Probe. Can the 125-Year-Old Agency Survive? *McClatchy – Tribune Business News*. Accessed March 23, 2021.

Assad, M. (2008, Jun 26). 4 critical errors identified in Kids Peace Death Investigation: Girls Stole Methadone From Worker, Report Says. *Morning Call*. Accessed on March 23, 2021.

Bahnaman, S. M. (2009). Ethics in professional life: Virtues for health and social care. *Choice Reviews*, 47(1), 146.

Baker, R., & Emanuel, L. (2000). The efficacy of professional ethics: The

AMA code of ethics in historical and current perspective. The Hastings Center Report, 30(4), S13-7.

Bedi, Neil (Sept 18, 2019). You're Trapped, They're Cashing In. How one Florida psychiatric hospital makes millions off patients who have no choice. *Tampa Bay Times*. Accessed on March 22, 2021.

Beauchamp, T. L., & Childress., J. F. (2013[1979]). Principles of biomedical ethics, seventh edition. New York: Oxford University Press

Benevento, M. (2021, Mar 11). Owners of Missouri Reform School Charged with more than 100 Felonies. *St.Louis Post – Dispatch*. Accessed on March 25, 2021.

Benoit,Wilfred J.,,Jr, & Nagle, J. W. (2003). Retaliation claims. *Employee Relations Law Journal*, 29(3), 13-72. Accessed on March 27, 2021

Bjørkelo, B., & Macko, M. (2012). The stigma of reporting wrongdoing at work: When doing right is perceived as wrong. *Polish Psychological Bulletin*, 43(2), 70.

Bodfield R. and, A. W. (1998, Mar 29). Increased reliance on private certification is criticized. *Arizona Daily Star*. Accessed on March 24, 2021.

Bouville, M. (2008). Whistle-blowing and morality: JBE. *Journal of Business Ethics, 81*(3), 579- 585.

Brown AJ. Whistleblowing in the Australian public sector: enhancing the theory and practice of internal witness management in public sector organizations. Canberra, Australia: ANU E Press; 2008.

Brys, Shannon. "Behavioral Healthcare Executive." BH FRAUD UPDATE: CRC Agrees to Resolve False Claims Act Allegations for $9.25 Million, 24 Apr. 2014. Accessed on March 22, 2021.

Cabrera, Ana & Weisfeldt, Sara (2014). Ex-patients, families say decades of abuse, fraud at Colorado facility ignored. CNN (website). Accessed on March 22, 2021.

Callahan, E. S., & Collins, J. W. (1992). Employee attitudes toward whistleblowing: Management and public policy implications: *JBE. Journal of Business Ethics*, 11(12), 939.

Carpenter, Jacob (January 9, 2016). Park Royal Hospital faces more trouble with lawsuit over suicide of psychiatric patient Theodore Ousback Jr. *Naples Daily News*. Accessed on March 22, 2021.

Cassematis, P. G., & Wortley, R. (2013). Prediction of whistleblowing or non-reporting observation: The role of personal and situational factors: *JBE. Journal of Business Ethics*, 117(3), 615-634.

Casler, Kristin. The Morning Call Reporter Ann Wlazelek contributed to this story. (1993, Nov 17). KIDSPEACE COUNSELOR CHARGED IN BOY'S DEATH: [FIFTH EDITION]. *Morning Call*. Accessed on March 26, 2021.

Caesar, N. (2006, 10). Qui tam suits on the rise. *HomeCare Magazine*, 29, 56.

Cheasty, M., Clare, A. W., & Collins, C. (1998). Relation between sexual abuse in childhood and adult depression: Case-control study. BMJ : *British Medical Journal*, 316(7126), 198.

Chen LP, Murad MH, Paras ML, Colbenson KM, Sattler AL, Goranson EN, Elamin MB, Seime RJ, Shinozaki G, Prokop LJ, Zirakzadeh A. Sexual abuse and lifetime diagnosis of psychiatric disorders: systematic review and meta-analysis. *Mayo Clinic Proceedings*. 2010 Jul;85(7):618-29.

Goranson, E. N., B.S., Zirakzadeh, A., M.D. (2010). Sexual abuse and lifetime diagnosis of psychiatric disorders: Systematic review and meta-analysis. *Mayo Clinic Proceedings*, 85(7), 618-29.

Chikomo, V. (2015, December 15). State Supreme Court affirms $122K judgment to nurse fired for not working overtime. *Pennsylvania Record*. Accessed on March 25, 2021.

Circelli, D. S. W. (2003, Mar 30). A shortage of foster care homes in Volusia and Flagler counties results in 67 children in state care being sent elsewhere, far from their families and schools; no place for children; shortage takes state wards far from home: [FINAL edition]. *Daytona Beach News - Journal, The.* Accessed on March 27, 2021.

Clancy, T. R. (2003). Courage and today's nurse leader. *Nursing Administration Quarterly*, 27(2), 128-32.

Cleverley, W. O., & Harvey, R. K. (1992). Is there a link between hospital profit and quality? *Healthcare Financial Management*, 46(9), 40-5.

Day L. Courage as a virtue necessary to good nursing practice. *American Journal of Critical Care (AJCC)*. 2007 Nov;16(6):613-6. PMID: 17962506.

DeVooght, K. & Blazey D. Family foster care reimbursement rates in the US: a report from a 2012 national survey on family foster care provider classification and rates. *Child Trends.* April 9, 2013

Eldeib, D. (2019, Dec 19). A Chicago psychiatric hospital is under fire after child abuse allegations. again. *ProPublica.* Accessed on April 10, 2021

Fandos, N. (2020, Aug 27). Brother of impeachment witness charges his firing was a whistleblower reprisal. *New York Times.*

Ferree, M. M., & Smith, E. R. (1979). A cognitive approach to social and individual stigma. The *Journal of Social Psychology*, 109, 87-97.

Fry, H. (2018). 100 workers at fountain valley regional hospital are set to strike Thursday. **Los Angeles Times (Online)**, Los Angeles: Los Angeles Times Communications LLC. Jan 31, 2018. Accessed on March 29, 2021.

Gardner, K. (2019, Feb 19). Kalispell regional healthcare hospital meets whistleblower settlement mandates. *TCA Regional News.* Accessed on March 26, 2021

Gartrell, N., Herman, J., Olarte, S., Feldstein, M., and Localio, R. (1986). Psychiatrist-patient contact: Results of a national survey, I: Prevalence. *American Journal of Psychaitry.* 143(9): 1126-1131.

Gaul, G. M. (2005, Jul 25). Accreditors blamed for overlooking problems; conflict of interest cited between health facilities, group that assesses conditions: [FINAL edition]. *The Washington Post.*

George, J. (2004, Feb 17). In mother's death, New Jersey man sees nurse's hand. *New York Times.*

Gechtman, L. (1989). Sexual contact between social workers and their clients. In G. O. Gabbard (Ed.), Sexual exploitation in professional relationships (pp. 27-38). Washington, DC: American Psychiatric Press.

Greene, R. (1998). The Explosive Child: A New Approach for Understanding and Parenting Easily Frustrated, Chronically Inflexible Children. New York: HarperCollins.

Greenwood CL, Tangalos EG, Maruta T. Prevalence of sexual abuse, physical abuse, and concurrent traumatic life events in a general medical population. Mayo Clin Proc. 1990 Aug;65(8):1067-71.

Goldberg, S. B. (1993, 07). Constructive Discharge. *ABA Journal*, 79, 87.

Greaves, R. & McGlone, J. (2012). The Health Consequences of Speaking Out. *Social Medicine.* Vol 6, No 4.

Greene, A. D., & Latting, J. K. (2004). Whistle-blowing as a form of advocacy: Guidelines for the practitioner and organization. *Social Work, 49*(2), 219-30.

Haiko Van, D. V., De Bruune, Mark, & Steenhuisen, B. (2019). Roles of risk managers: Understanding how risk managers engage in regulation. *European Journal of Risk Regulation* : EJRR, 10(2), 376-392.

Hallam, K. (1997, Jun 03). Hospital accrediting process due for surgery, critics say. *Nashville Banner.*

Hamacher, H. (2017, Jan 30). Top verdicts of 2016. *North Carolina Lawyers Weekly.*

Hayes, M. J., Geiger, J. M., & Lietz, C. A. (2015). Navigating a complicated system of care: Foster parent satisfaction with behavioral and medical health services: C & A. *Child & Adolescent Social Work Journal*, 32(6), 493-505.

Hilzenrath, D. S. (1998, Dec 31). Justice dept. joins suit against Columbia/HCA; whistle-blower alleges Medicare fraud. *The Washington Post*.

Hirst, S. P. (2002). Defining resident abuse within the culture of long-term care institutions. *Clinical Nursing Research*, 11(3), 267-84.

Hobbs, G. F., Hobbs, C. J., & Wynne, J. M. (1999). Abuse of children in foster and residential care. *Child Abuse & Neglect*, 23(12), 1239-1252.

Holden, M. J., & Sellers, D. (2019). An Evidence-Based Program Model for Facilitating Therapeutic Responses to Pain-Based Behavior in Residential Care. *International Journal of Child, Youth & Family Studies*, 10(2-3), 63-80.

Holman, G. J. (2021, Mar 11). Ranch owners charged with child abuse, rape, molestation. *Springfield News Leader*.

Hoffman, W. M., Neill, J. D., & Stovall, O. S. (2008). An investigation of ethics officer independence: JBE. *Journal of Business Ethics*, 78(1-2), 87-95.

Hummer, V. L., Dollard, N., Robst, J., & Armstrong, M. I. (2010). Innovations in implementation of trauma-informed care practices in youth residential treatment: A curriculum for organizational change. *Child Welfare*, 89(2), 79-95.

Hutchinson, S. C. (1991). Sexual contact between therapist and client: A survey of social workers in private practice. Unpublished doctoral dissertation, Tulane University, School of Social Work, New Orleans.

Indira A.R. Lakshmanan, Globe Staff. (1995, May 25). Agency admits missteps in 2nd rape case; shortage of homes blamed for `stretch' in foster placement: [city edition]. *Boston Globe* (pre-1997 full text). Accessed on March 29, 2021.

Iseminger, Karen, PhD,R.N., F.N.P. (2010). Overview and summary: Moral courage amid moral distress: Strategies for action. *Online Journal of Issues in Nursing*, 15(3), 4-1D,2D,3D,4D.

Jackall, R. (1991). Jackall, Robert. moral mazes: The world of corporate managers // review. Canadian Banker, 98(3), 62-63.

Jackson, D. (MAR 07, 2019, 6 women sexually abused by counselor at women's rehab center Timberline Knolls, prosecutors say. *Chicago Tribune*. Accessed on March 22, 2021.

Jackson, D. (2011, May 18). Report faults care of young psychiatric patients at Chicago Lakeshore Hospital. *McClatchy - Tribune Business News*.

Jackson, D., & Marx, G. (2010, Sep 22). Kids sexually assaulted at psychiatric hospitals, reports say. *McClatchy - Tribune Business News*.

Jackson, D., Peters, K., Andrew, S., Edenborough, M., Halcomb, E., Luck, L., Wilkes, L. (2010).

Trial and retribution: A qualitative study of whistleblowing and workplace relationships in nursing. *Contemporary Nurse: A Journal for the Australian Nursing Profession*, 36(1), 34-44.

Jayaratne, S., Croxton, T., & Mattison, D. (1997). Social work professional standards: An exploratory study. *Social Work*, 42, 187-199.

Jeremy, C., Ann, P., Wai-Shan, C., Richardson, J., Stirling, M., & Feder, G. (2003). Abusive experiences and psychiatric morbidity in women primary care attenders. *The British Journal of Psychiatry*, 183(4), 332-339.

Johnstone, M. (2004). Patient safety, ethics and whistleblowing: A nursing response to the events at the Campbelltown and Camden hospitals. *Australian Health Review*, 28(1), 13-9.

Jameson, M. (2013, Apr 15). Halifax hospital whistleblower at forefront of $200M alleged fraud. *McClatchy - Tribune Business News*

Jameton, A. (1993). Dilemmas of moral distress: Moral responsibility and nursing practice. *AWHONNS Clinical Issues Perinatal Women's Health Nursing*, 4, 542-551.

Jonsen, A. R. & Jameton, A.L. (1977). Social and political responsibilities of physicians, *The Journal of Medicine and Philosophy: A Forum for Bioethics and Philosophy of Medicine*, 2(4), 376–400.

Kanno-Youngs, Z., & Goldman, A. (2020, Sep 11). Whistleblower's complaint ignites a smoldering homeland security agency. *New York Times*.

Kenny, K., Fotaki, M., & Scriver, S. (2019). Mental health as a weapon: Whistleblower retaliation and normative violence: JBE. *Journal of Business Ethics*, 160(3), 801-815.

Khalil, D. D.,PhD.M.A.B.A.R.N.R.M.R.N.T. (2009). Nurses' attitude towards 'difficult' and 'good' patients in eight public hospitals. *International Journal of Nursing Practice*, 15(5), 437.

Kidder, R.M. (2005). *Moral Courage*. New York, NY: Harper Collins Publishers.

Kohn, Stephen Martin. NEW WHISTLEBLOWER'S HANDBOOK: a Step-by-Step Guide to Doing What's Right and Protecting Yourself. LYONS PR, 2021.

Knoll, Allen (2018). Surviving Bethel: A True Story. Amazon Publishing

Lachs M, Pillemer K: Abuse and neglect of elderly persons. *New England Journal of Medicine* 1995, 332:437–443.

Lam, M. B., Figueroa, J. F., Feyman, Y., Reimold, K. E., Orav, E. J., & Jha, A. K. (2018). Association

between patient outcomes and accreditation in US hospitals: Observational study. BMJ : *British Medical Journal* (Online), 363

LaSala, Cynthia Ann,M.S., R.N., & Bjarnason, Dana, PhD,R.N., N.E.-B.C. (2010). Creating workplace environments that support moral courage:

[1]. *Online Journal of Issues in Nursing*, 15(3), 10-1F,2F,3F,4F,5F,6F,7F,8 F,9F,10F Levine, Art. "Dark Side of a Bain Success." *Salon*, Salon.com, 18 July 2012. Accessed on March 22,2021.

Lewis, K., & Gardner, S. (2000). Looking for Dr. Jekyll but hiring Mr. Hyde: Preventing negligent hiring, supervision, retention, and training. *Hospital Topics*, 78(1), 14-22.

Lieberman, T. (2017, Oct 04). Hospitals may get accredited even with poor, unsafe care. *Chicago Citizen*.

Lovern, E. (2001). JCAHO database role worries AHA. *Modern Health-care*, 31(33), 4-5. Maciejewski, P. K., & Mazure, C. M. (2006). Fear of criticism and rejection mediates an association between childhood emotional abuse and adult onset of major depression. *Cognitive Therapy and Research*, 30(1), 105-122.

Major, Z. B. (2018). Struggle for Integrity In Residential Children's Homes: Professional Self-Esteem and Organizational Development — Practical Experiences from Hungary. *International Journal of Child, Youth & Family Studies*, 9(2), 1-27.

Makary M A, Daniel M. (2016). Medical error—the third leading cause of death in the US. *British Medical Journal*. 353: i2139

Maluwa, V. M., Andre, J., Ndebele, P., & Chilemba, E. (2012). Moral distress in nursing practice in Malawi. *Nursing Ethics*, 19(2), 196-207.

Mansbach, A., & Bachner, Y. G. (2010). Internal or external whistleblowing: Nurses' willingness to report wrongdoing. *Nursing Ethics*, 17(4), 483-90.

Marcus, R. (2005, Jun 05). 'It was not I'; It's hard to believe W. Mark Felt had this kind of exposure in mind.: [FINAL edition]. *The Washington Post*. Accessed on March, 24, 2021.

Martinez, M. M. (2000, May 11). Foster parent shortage more children than caregivers. Agencies struggle to keep and recruit foster families. *Austin American Statesman*

Martucci, W. C., & Clemow, D. D. (1995). Workplace violence: Incidents - and liability - on the rise. *Employment Relations Today*, 21(4), 463.

Mayo, Bob. "4 Lawsuits Allege Abuse at McGuire Memorial, Including 2 Wrongful Deaths." Pittsburgh Action News 4, 22 Nov. 2019. Accessed on March 25, 2021.

McDonald, Sally,R.N., M.N., & Ahern, K., PhD. (2002). Physical and emotional effects of whistle blowing. *Journal of Psychosocial Nursing & Mental Health Services*, 40(1), 14-27.

McKinney, M. (2010). Rebound at Joint Commission. *Modern Healthcare*, 40(48), 17.

Miceli, M. P., & Near, J. P. (2002). What makes whistleblowers effective? Three field studies. *Human Relations*, 55(4), 455-479.

Mitchell, K. (2012, May 12). Lawsuits allege Wheat Ridge teen treatment center lied to patients, fostered rifts with parents. *Denver Post*. Accessed on March 22, 2021

Mole, B. (2017). Hundreds of hospitals with violations, deaths get "gold seal of approval." New York: Condé Nast Publications, Inc.

Morley, G., Ives, J., & Bradbury-Jones, C. (2019). Moral distress and austerity: An avoidable ethical challenge in healthcare. *Health Care Analysis*: HCA, 27(3), 185-201.

Murray, John S, PhD, RN,U.S.A.F.,N.C. (2010). Moral courage in healthcare: Acting ethically even in the presence of risk. *Online Journal of Issues in Nursing*, 15(3), 9-1G,2G,3G,4G,5G,6G,7G,8G,9G.

Nadi, A., Rappleye , H., Riordan Saville, L. and Winter, Tom (Oct. 17, 2013) Camps for troubled kids can be magnets for abuse. *NBC News*. Accessed on March 26, 2021.

Near JP, Miceli MP. Organizational dissidence: the case of whistleblowing. *Journal of Business Ethics*. 1985;4:1-16.

Noel, M. M. (1988). Reporting colleagues who are sexually intimate with clients: It's time to talk. *Women & Therapy*, 7(2-3), 87–94.

Norma, S. H. (2006). Blowing the whistle on healthcare fraud: Should I? *Journal of the American Academy of Nurse Practitioners*, 18(11), 512-7.

O'Hanlon, A. (2000, Jul 06). Shortage of foster parents forces rigorous recruiting; county bucks problem seen by its neighbors: [FINAL edition]. *The Washington Post.* Accessed on March 27, 2021

Parker, C. (2014, May 13). WaPo panel discusses NSA surveillance program and ongoing revelations (posted 2014-05-13 08:10:10): On April 23, the post hosted a panel discussion with reporters behind its Pulitzer-Prize-winning stories on the NSA surveillance program. *The Washington Post.*

Peternelj-Taylor, C., & Yonge, O. (2003). Exploring boundaries in the nurse-client relationship: Professional roles and responsibilities. *Perspectives in Psychiatric Care*, 39(2), 55-66.

Peterson, I., & Reporting for this article was contributed by Stacey Stowe, and Janon Fisher. Jason George. (2003, Dec 13). Nurse facing inquiry was forced out at 3 hospitals. *New York Times.*

Polnay, L., Glaser, A., & Rao, V. (1996). Better health for children in resident care. *Archives of Disease in Childhood*, 75(3), 263.

Prager, L. O. (1999). IG report: Joint commission too chummy with hospitals. *American Medical News*, 42(30), 8-8, 10.

Reader, T. W., & Gillespie, A. (2013). Patient neglect in healthcare institutions: A systematic review and conceptual model. *BMC Health Services Research*, 13, 156.

Reamer, F. G. (1998). The evolution of social work ethics. *Social Work*, 43(6), 488-500.

Reamer, F. G. (1995). Malpractice claims against social workers: First facts. *Social Work*, 40, 595601.

Riddick, F. A. (2003). The code of medical ethics of the American Medical Association. *The Ochsner Journal*, 5(2), 6-10.

Robinson, R. K., Novicevic, M., & Nichols, D. L. (2014). Expanding Protection for Whistleblowers Under Federal Employment Laws: A Primer on Retaliation. *Southern Law Journal*, 24(2), 221-235.

Rickert, Chris (2007, Nov 13). How Much Money Is Enough for Foster Care?: Reimbursing Foster Parents; A Study Finds that Wisconsin doesn't Pay Enough; Local Foster Parents have Mixed Opinions about the Reimbursement Rate. *Wisconsin State Journal*.

Rothschild, J., & Miethe, T. D. (1999). Whistleblower disclosures and management retaliation: The battle to control information about organization corruption. *Work and Occupations*, 26(1), 107-128.

Rucker, Philip - Washington Post, Staff Writer. (2007, Oct 28). In U.S., foster care funding in 'crisis'; only D.C. and Arizona reimburse families adequately, U-MD. study finds: [FINAL edition]. *The Washington Post*.

Ruhnka, J. C., Gac, E. J., & Boerstler, H. (2000). Qui tam claims: Threat to voluntary compliance programs in health care organizations. *Journal of Health Politics, Policy and Law*, 25(2), 283-308.

Sheffer, J. (2018). 'Everyone in healthcare is a risk manager': Achieving risk-savvy cultures. *Biomedical Instrumentation & Technology*, 52(1), 50-58.

Schindler, Randy RN (2019) HealthCare Disasters: Hospital Overlords Put Profits Before Patients & Kill Thousands - A First Hand Whistleblower Account. Amazon Press. (October 16, 2019)

Schluter, J., Winch, S., Holzhauser, K., & Henderson, A. (2008). Nurses' moral sensitivity and hospital ethical climate: A literature review. *Nursing Ethics*, 15(3), 304-21.

Soeken KL, Soeken DR. A survey of whistleblowers: their stressors and coping strategies. Laurel, Maryland: Association of Mental Health Specialties; 1986. Accessed December 8, 2020.

Stake, J. E., & Oliver, J. (1991). Sexual contact and touching between therapist and client: A survey of psychologists' attitudes and behavior. *Professional Psychology: Research and Practice*, 22(4), 297–307.

Stensland M, Watson PR, Grazier KL. An examination of costs, charges, and payments for inpatient psychiatric treatment in community hospitals. Psychiatry Services (online). 2012 Jul;63(7):666-71.

Strout TD. Perspectives on the experience of being physically restrained: an integrative review of the qualitative literature. *International Journal of Mental Health Nursing.* 2010 Dec;19(6):416-27. PMID: 21054728.

Sturm, R., Ringel, J., Bao, Y., Stein, B., Kapur, K., Zhang, W., & Zeng, F. (2001). Mental Health Care for Youth: Who Gets It? How Much Does It Cost? Who Pays? Where Does the Money Go?. Santa Monica, CA: RAND Corporation, 2001.

Sundram CJ. Obstacles to reducing patient abuse in public institutions. *Hospital Community Psychiatry.* 1984 Mar; 35(3):238-43. PMID: 6706325.

Suttles, Chrissy. "Former McGuire Memorial Employee Pleads Guilty to Dozens of Charges." *Ellwood City Ledger*, 27 Feb. 2020. Accessed on March 28, 2021.

Swisher, S. (2014, Mar 22). Whistleblower behind Halifax Health lawsuit says she's been 'shunned'. Daytona Beach News - Journal, the. Accessed on March 26, 2021.

Taylor, M. (1999). Healthcare tattletales. *Modern Healthcare*, 29(47), 30-32+.

VerHelst, Megan. Police Raid Mental Health Hospital, Dozens of Complaints Filed. *Patch.* Dec 6, 2019. Accessed on March 28, 2021.

Waldman, J, D.., Smith, H. L., & Hood, J. N. (2003). Corporate culture: The missing piece of the healthcare puzzle. *Hospital Topics*, 81(1), 5-14.

Washburn, D. The Morning Call Staff writer Christine Schiavo contributed to this report. (1999, Mar 28). Methods of Restraining Young Patients Questioned Deaths from Subduing Troubled Youths Bring Call for Proper Training, Review by Legislatures and Agencies: [SECOND EDITION]. *Morning Call*.

Watts, L. L., & Buckley, M. R. (2017). A dual-processing model of moral whistleblowing in organizations: JBE. *Journal of Business Ethics*, 146(3), 669-683.

Wecheli, Andreae (1595). "Hippocrates. Τα ενρισκομενα Opera omnia». Frankfurt: National Institute of Health; National Library of Medicine; History of Medicine Division).

Wise, L. A., Zierier, S., Krieger, N., & Harlow, B. L. (2001). Adult onset of major depressive disorder in relation to early life violent victimization: A case-control study. *The Lancet*, 358(9285), 881-7.

Additional Citations:

CRC health group to be acquired by Acadia Healthcare: Combined company will offer a broad spectrum of behavioral health services. (2014, Oct 29). PR Newswire. Accessed on March 29, 2021.

Hospital credentials don't mean much. (1996, Jul 15). Morning Star. Accessed on March 29, 2021.

How do whistleblower advocates deal with Edward Snowden's case? (posted 2013-06-25 13:39:28): The Snowden case presents critical e questions for whistleblower advocates. (2013, Jun 25). *The Washington Post*. Accessed on March 28, 2021.

Justice department: Home health agency, former owner to pay $5.8 million to settle false claims act allegations. (2020, Nov 20). *Targeted News Service*.

AMA Website

National Association of Social Workers – Social Work Code of Ethics (2021).

National Association of Social Workers – Social Work Code of Ethics (1979).

American Medical Association Website. Accessed on 4/28/2021.

The Joint Commission Website. Accessed on 4/28/2021.

Department of Justice Press Release 2003 (p. 66). Accessed on 4/21/2021

Index

CPSIA information can be obtained
at www.ICGtesting.com
Printed in the USA
BVHW041032191021
619300BV00018B/314